はしがき

　物事を成就させるためには、その過程こそが大切です。『seek next 英語総合問題 SECOND EDITION』シリーズは、日頃の基礎固めの英語学習から、さらに受験に対応する力までを養成するために編集された総合問題集です。当シリーズは、各学習段階に応じた5冊から成り、「文法」「作文」「リスニング」「速読」「長文読解」を中心とした構成となっています。

　このシリーズの2冊目にあたる本書『seek next 2 SECOND EDITION』は、文法体系に基づく展開で、各レッスンの文法事項を軸として学習を進められるようにしています。各レッスンの「文法」の文法事項が「作文」「長文読解」へと連動しており、文法事項を確実に定着できるように工夫しています。

　また、各レッスンの「リスニング」と「速読」では、「長文読解」と同じテーマや、関連したテーマの英文を収録しています。リスニングや掲示、ウェブサイト、広告などのさまざまな読み物を通して、「長文読解」の題材に関する知識を深めることができるようにしています

JN102706

本書の構成と特色

各レッスンは4ページ構成で、全部で15レッスンから成っています。各レッスンを「文法」➡「作文」➡「リスニング」➡「速読」➡「長文読解」の流れで構成しました。

■ Grammar
●必ず習得するべき重要項目を厳選し、文法体系に基づいて15レッスンに配しました。

■ Writing
●各レッスンの文法事項をふまえた部分整序作文問題もしくは英訳完成問題です。Grammar と連動した問題内容です。

■ Listening
●各レッスンの「長文読解」と同じテーマの英文を聞き取ります。
●さまざまな試験の形式に対応した問題を収録しています。
● (🔊) は、教師用付属の音声 CD のトラック番号を示します。二次元コードを読み取って、音声をPC やスマートフォンなどから聞くこともできます。

■ Rapid Reading
●各レッスンの「長文読解」と同じテーマの英文を収録しています。
●ふつうの英文だけでなく、掲示、広告、メールなどの読み取り問題など、さまざまな形式の問題を収録しています。

■ Reading
●各レッスンの文法事項を含んだ長文読解問題です。興味を引く題材、知的好奇心を喚起する題材、SDGs に対応した題材を選びました。
●各レッスンの「リスニング」と「速読」と同じテーマの英文を収録しています。
●速読問題：設定された時間内に本文を読み、本文の要旨や概要についての理解を問う問題としました。
●精読問題：本文の内容上の重要箇所に関する問題や文法事項を含む問題、本文全体に関する内容把握問題から成ります。

CAN-DO List
●各レッスンの学習の到達目標を「知識・技能」、「思考力・判断力・表現力」の観点から示しています。満点が取れたら、□にチェックを入れましょう。

Contents

Rapid Reading		Reading		
テーマ	問題形式			
客船	GTEC®	タイタニック号に乗りそこねた家族。		210 words
教育	英検®	女子教育の重要性。		222 words
自動車	英検®	自動車からの排出ガス削減の取り組み。		191 words
ファッション	共通テスト	ファッション産業と環境問題のつながり。		218 words
家族	GTEC®	子供が家出をしたがったら。		243 words
お金	英検®	世の中に普及したクレジットカード。		220 words
意見	GTEC®	盲目の兄弟がゾウを触ったら。		276 words
仕事	英検®	ある日本人が生み出した缶コーヒー。		249 words
レストラン	GTEC®	クレームが生み出したヒット商品。		263 words
家族		両親の愛情表現の違い。		245 words
情報化社会		フェイクニュースに向き合う力。		297 words
旅行	GTEC®	画期的な旅行会社を創業した人物。		292 words
動物	共通テスト	ペットセラピーについて。		251 words
情報化社会	英検®	現代の情報社会で生きるために。		246 words
自転車	GTEC®	自転車の利用を推進する取り組み。		274 words

Lesson 1 文の種類

Grammar 目標 ➡ 7分

1 次の各文の下線部をたずねる疑問文を作りなさい。 (各3点)

1. This word means "very bad."

   _____

2. They want to go to Hawaii for vacation.

   _____

3. Tom is leaving town at the end of this month.

   _____

4. They have lived here for 10 years.

   _____

2 次の疑問文を、与えられた書き出しに続けて文を完成させなさい。 (各3点)

1. Why did he go home early?

   I don't know _____ .

2. Where is the museum?

   Can you tell me _____ ?

3. What was Ann wearing at the party?

   Do you remember _____ ?

Writing 目標 ➡ 5分

3 ( )内に与えられた語句を並べかえて、英文を完成しなさい。 (各4点)

1. フットボールのチームには何人の選手がいますか。

   How (are / many / on / players / there) a football team?

   _____

2. 会合は何時に始まるか知っていますか。

   Do you (begins / know / the meeting / time / what)?

   _____

3. ジョンはどうしていつも学校に遅れるのかしら。

   I wonder (always / John / is / late / why) for school.

   _____

CAN-DO List □ 🎧 〈知識・技能〉疑問詞を使った疑問文、間接疑問文を適切に活用することができる。

4 それぞれの写真について 4 つの説明が読まれます。写真に最も合っているものを、一つずつ選びなさい。 (各 5 点)

1.  　① ② ③ ④

2.  　① ② ③ ④

Rapid Reading 　目標 ➡ 5分 　　　　　　　　　　テーマ 客船 GTEC®

5 広告を読み取って、問いに対する答えとして最も適当なものを一つずつ選びなさい。 (各 5 点)

DISCOUNT ON ALL CRUISE CATEGORIES

   Sydney Cruise is offering discounted cruises this year. During its 14-day roundtrip cruises from Australia, the 125-meter long passenger vessel will allow guests to explore nine islands and enjoy Sydney city.

   Guests can book and save on the following departures:

Room type	Price	Departure date	Discount rate
premium suite	$7800 per person	13 January, 12 June	5%
		29 March, 2 October	10%
royal suite	$8500 per person	13 January, 12 June	5%
		29 March, 2 October	10%

Onboard Activities & Entertainment

   Swimming pools (7 a.m. till 9 p.m.)

   Spas (open 11 a.m. till 6 p.m.)

   Fitness center (open 24 hrs)

   Table tennis (From 1 p.m.)

   Cooking demonstrations (At 10 a.m. and 3 p.m.)

   Live music (From 6 p.m.)

   Cinema (At 1 p.m., 3 p.m. and 7 p.m.)

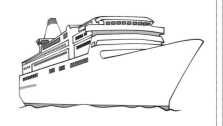

---

1. How much would it cost for a couple to go on the cruise in a premium room on 29 March?

  ① $14040 　　② $14820 　　③ $15300 　　④ $16150

2. What activity is available in the morning?

  ① Swimming. 　② Table tennis. 　③ Live music. 　④ Cinema.

Reading 目標 ➡20分 文法項目 間接疑問文 テーマ 客船   4

速 読問題 次の英文を2.5分で読んで、1. の問いに答えなさい。

This is a story about the Clark family. The Clark family lived in Scotland about a

hundred years ago. Mr. Clark, the father, had (1)a dream. He wanted to take his family

to the United States. He wanted to give his wife and nine children a new life. So,

Mr. Clark worked hard and saved money. (2)It took many years, but he finally saved

5 enough money to go to the United States. He bought tickets to travel on a new ship

that was leaving for the United States in a few days.

Then, something terrible happened. Mr. Clark's youngest son was bitten by a dog.

The doctor told the family that they had to stay at home. (3)They could not leave their

house for 14 days, so they could not get on the ship. Mr. Clark watched the ship *sail

10 away on the ocean, and (4)he cried. He lost his dream.

Then (5)five days later, something more terrible happened. (6)News came to Scotland

that Mr. Clark's ship hit an *iceberg and sank. Many people died. You may know

what the name of the ship was. Yes, it was *the Titanic. Mr. Clark then realized that

the *misfortune of his son had saved them. He went home and *hugged his son.

(210 words)

⁹sail [séɪl]：(船が)航行する　　¹²iceberg [áɪsbə̀ːrg]：氷山
¹³the Titanic：タイタニック号(1912年、大西洋上で沈没した英国の豪華客船)
¹⁴misfortune [mɪsfɔ́ːrtʃ(ə)n]：不運、災難　　¹⁴hug [hʌ́g]：…をしっかりと抱きしめる

CAN-DO List ☐ 〈知識・技能〉間接疑問文について理解できる。
☐ 〈思考力・判断力・表現力〉タイタニック号とある家族に関するストーリーの展開を的確に理解することができる。

1. この英文で主に述べられているものを、次のa.〜d.から選びなさい。 （5点）

    a. 幸運の女神は努力する人にほほえむ。

    b. 不運か幸運かは予測できない。

    c. 不運は重なるものである。

    d. 不運もうまく活用すれば幸運となる。

精 読問題 もう一度英文を読んで、次の問いに答えなさい。

2. 下線部(1)の具体的な内容を、日本語で簡潔に説明しなさい。 （6点）

3. 下線部(2)について、何をするのに「何年もかかった」のですか。日本語で説明しなさい。 （6点）

4. 下線部(3)の理由を、日本語で説明しなさい。 （5点）

5. 下線部(4)について、次の問いに英語で答えなさい。 （6点）

    Why did he cry?

6. 下線部(5)の解釈として最も適当なものを、次のa.〜c.から選びなさい。 （3点）

    a. five days after Mr. Clark bought tickets to travel on a new ship

    b. five days after Mr. Clark's youngest son was bitten by a dog

    c. five days after Mr. Clark watched the ship sail away on the ocean

7. 文法 下線部(6)の具体的な内容を、日本語で説明しなさい。 （6点）

8. 全体把握 本文の内容と合っているものにはT、合っていないものにはFと答えなさい。 （各2点）

    (ア) クラーク氏は、家族を愛している勤勉な父親であった。 （　　　）

    (イ) クラーク氏は、アメリカへ向かう船の切符を手に入れるのに2、3日かかった。 （　　　）

    (ウ) クラーク一家は、アメリカへ向かう船に乗り遅れた。 （　　　）

    (エ) クラーク氏は、乗る予定であった船の名前がタイタニック号であるとは知らなかった。

    （　　　）

    (オ) クラーク氏の息子がイヌにかまれたことが、船の沈没の原因となった。 （　　　）

Lesson 2 文型

Grammar　目標 ➡ 7分

1 （　　）内に、下の a.～ e. から適当なものを選び、記号を補いなさい。　　　　（各2点）

1. The train for Oxford leaves (　　　　).
2. The shops downtown keep (　　　　).
3. Power from the car engine turns (　　　　).
4. Ellen's parents will give (　　　　).
5. A refrigerator keeps (　　　　).

　　a. from Platform 4　　　　　　　　b. her a bicycle for Christmas

　　c. open late on Friday evenings　　d. meat fresh　　　　　　　e. the wheels

2 （　　）内に、下の a.～ d. から適当なものを選び、記号を補いなさい。　　　　（各2点）

1. Let's go to the shopping center.　I need (　　　　).
2. Do you believe (　　　　)?
3. The girl in the shop asked me (　　　　).
4. I took the examination on Friday, but I don't know (　　　　).

　　a. if I passed it　　　　　　　　b. that there is life after death

　　c. to buy a few things　　　　　d. what I wanted to buy

Writing　目標 ➡ 5分

3 （　　）内に与えられた語句を並べかえて、英文を完成しなさい。　　　　（各4点）

1. 彼らの手紙によると、彼らは月曜日にやって来るそうです。

　　Their letter (arrive / says / that / they / will) on Monday.

　　_____

2. 世界中に何人の人がいるか知っていますか。

　　Do you know (are / how / many / people / there) in the world?

　　_____

3. 父が家にいるかどうかわかりません。　I don't know (at / home / if / is / my father).

　　_____

4. 彼がネクタイをしていたかどうか覚えていません。

　　I don't remember (a tie / he / if / was / wearing).

　　_____

CAN-DO List　□　〈知識・技能〉5文型、S＋V＋O（to-不定詞、節）、S＋V＋O＋O（節）を適切に活用することができる。

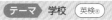

4 それぞれのイラストについて対話と応答を聞き、最後の発言に対する応答として最も適当なものを一つずつ選びなさい。 (各5点)

1.  ① ② ③ ④

2.  ① ② ③ ④

Rapid Reading 目標 ➡ 5分  テーマ 教育 英検®

5 （1）・（2）に入れるのに最も適当なものを一つずつ選びなさい。 (各5点)

I went to a university to enjoy the open day with Kazuha and Reika.　In the morning, we experienced a university lecture in a classroom about the history of England.　Reika said it was interesting.　But Kazuha and I couldn't enjoy it very much because (1) history.　After that, we had lunch at the cafeteria on campus.　The *atmosphere inside was very nice, and (2).　In the afternoon, a university student volunteer showed us around the campus.　I enjoyed the open day very much and am looking forward to being a university student.

---

⁴ atmosphere [ǽtməsfiər]：雰囲気

1. ① she wanted to study
   ② they didn't like
   ③ three of us all loved
   ④ we aren't good at
2. ① other students didn't like it
   ② the cafeteria wasn't open then
   ③ the meal was delicious
   ④ we had a big breakfast

Reading　目標➡20分　文法項目 S＋V＋O（＝that-節）　テーマ 教育　◀)) 7

速 読問題 次の英文を2.5分で読んで、1. の問いに答えなさい。

In most countries of the world including Japan, (1)children going to school every day is a familiar scene. However, for more than 72 million children around the world, school is a *luxury they cannot enjoy. This is especially true for girls.

One reason for (2)this imbalance between genders is that, in many communities, males
5　are more highly valued than females. In such communities, girls are expected to marry young and have children. Education costs an average of $1.25 a day per child in developing countries. Thus, (3)parents with little money to spare tend to send their sons to school but keep their daughters at home. They may believe that it would be a waste of money to pay for their daughters to attend school.

10　However, educating girls today can help future generations. One reason is that schools can *provide girls with life skills and knowledge about *reproductive health. According to (4)UNESCO data, if all girls in developing countries completed elementary school, child *mortality would drop by 20%. In addition, *maternal deaths would be reduced by almost 70%. Another reason is that girls are the future mothers of any
15　society. Every girl that receives an education is more likely to make education a *priority for her children.

For these reasons, *ensuring a basic education for girls leads to positive change in the community.

(222 words)

---

³luxury [lʌ́ɡʒ(ə)ri]：ぜいたく品　　¹¹provide A with B：AにBを提供する
¹¹reproductive health：性と生殖に関する健康　　¹³mortality [mɔːrtǽləti]：死亡率
¹³maternal [mətə́ːrn(ə)l]：妊婦の　　¹⁶priority [praɪɔ́ːrəti]：優先事項
¹⁷ensure [ɪnʃʊ́ər]：…を保証する

CAN-DO List　☐ 〈知識・技能〉S＋V＋O（that-節）について理解できる。
☐ 〈思考力・判断力・表現力〉女子教育に関する格差について的確に理解できる。

1. この英文のタイトルとして最も適当なものを、次のa.～d.から選びなさい。　　　（5点）

   a. Educating More Girls Leads to a Better Society

   b. How Can We Change Education in Developed Countries?

   c. The Discussion of Gender Imbalance

   d. Why Are Women in Developing Countries Less Valued?

精 読問題 もう一度英文を読んで、次の問いに答えなさい。

2. 下線部(1)と対照的な内容を述べている箇所を、本文中から7語で抜き出しなさい。　（7点）

_____

3. 下線部(2)は具体的にどのような状況ですか。日本語で説明しなさい。　　　　　（8点）

_____

4. 文法 下線部(3)のように親たちが判断するのは、彼らが娘を学校に行かせることについてどう考えているからですか。日本語で説明しなさい。　　　　　　　　　　　　　　　　　　（7点）

_____

5. 下線部(4)について、空欄に語句を記入して、示されている仮説を完成させなさい。　（完答4点）

  すべての女子が小学校を卒業すれば、（　　　　　　　　）の死亡率と（　　　　　　　　）の死亡数が減るだろうということ。

6. 第3パラグラフの内容を前半部と後半部に分けるとき、後半部の先頭となる語を本文中から抜き出しなさい。　　　　　　　　　　　　　　　　　　　　　　　　　　　　　　　　　　　　（5点）

  （　　　　　　　）

7. 全体把握 本文の内容と合っているものにはT、合っていないものにはFと答えなさい。（各2点）

  (ア) Over 70 million boys and girls in the world can't go to school.　　　（　　　　　）

  (イ) Girls in developing countries want to marry young.　　　（　　　　　）

  (ウ) Schools with more girls and fewer boys are ideal.　　　（　　　　　）

  (エ) Child mortality has already dropped in developing countries.　　　（　　　　　）

  (オ) Education for girls might change negative situations in the community.

                                   （　　　　　）

Lesson 3 時制①

Grammar 目標➡7分

1 ( )内に下記の語群から適語を選び、過去分詞にして補いなさい。 (各2点)

1. I have ( ) my key.　I can't find it.

2. They don't live here anymore.　They have ( ) to Kobe.

3. I haven't ( ) to Paris, but I've ( ) pictures of the Eiffel Tower.

4. My mother has never ( ) by plane.

【be / lose / move / see / travel】

2 ( )内の語句をつけ加えて、「ずっと…だ」という現在完了形の文を作りなさい。3.と4.は、現在完了進行形(have [has] been ～ing)にしなさい。 (各3点)

1. They live in this town.　(for ten years)

_____

2. Mr. Brown is in the hospital.　(since the accident)

_____

3. It is snowing.　(for three days)

_____

4. I am waiting here for Mary.　(since seven o'clock)

_____

Writing 目標➡5分

3 ( )内に適語を補って、英文を完成しなさい。 (各3点)

1. その事故のことはお父さんにもう話しましたか。

Have you ( ) your father about the accident ( )?

2. お金を払わないでレストランを出たことがありますか。

Have you ( ) left a restaurant ( ) paying the bill?

3. ジムとはいつからの知り合いですか。

How ( ) have you ( ) Jim?

4. ピーターを起こしてください。もう10時間も眠っているのですから。

Please wake Peter.　He has ( ) ( ) for ten hours.

4 英語を聞き、それぞれの内容と最もよく合うイラストを一つずつ選びなさい。　(各5点)

1.

① The garbage on the beach　② The garbage on the beach　③ The garbage on the beach　④ The garbage on the beach

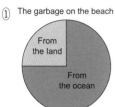　

2.

 ① Driver's seat : Right　 ② Driver's seat : Left　 ③ Driver's seat : Right　 ④ Driver's seat : Right

Rapid Reading　目標 ➡ 5分　テーマ 自動車 英検®

5 （1）・（2）に入るのに最も適当なものを一つずつ選びなさい。　(各5点)

Car Tax in Japan

As in other countries, car owners in Japan, both for private and business use, must pay a car tax per vehicle every year.　The amount of tax （　1　） according to the engine size.　The bigger the engine size is, the higher the tax will be.　That is the basic car tax system in Japan.　But, you will have to pay a much higher amount in addition to the basic tax if your car is thirteen years old or older.　*On the contrary, the car tax （　2　） if you own a new eco-friendly one.

6 on the contrary：それに対して

1. ① is all the same
   ② is different
   ③ will be late
   ④ will decide
2. ① can be paid by credit card
   ② has to be paid
   ③ might be expensive
   ④ will be discounted

速読問題 次の英文を2.5分で読んで、1. の問いに答えなさい。

Private cars are responsible for about 11% of the world's total carbon dioxide *emissions. The *transport sector *accounts for 24% of emissions overall, so private cars emit the most carbon dioxide in this sector.   *Petrol and diesel cars are associated with (1)many other harmful effects, such as air pollution, *congestion and accidents.   It

5 is clear that (2)these cars must be largely removed from the roads to achieve *sustainable mobility.

  (3)The good news is that some policies have been *enacted to reduce *greenhouse-gas emissions and air pollution from petrol and diesel cars.   Some markets have tightened emissions limits.

10   The bad news is that more than 99% of new passenger cars sold worldwide still rely on fossil fuels, and overall vehicle ownership in Europe grew by 25% between 2000 and 2017.   The continued demand for vehicle ownership *stems from several factors, such as increased income and more mobility as people travel farther to their jobs as a result of (4)greater city *sprawl.   (5)The *transition away from traditional vehicles is *hindered

15 by the high costs of electric cars.   In addition, *potential owners of electric cars have "*range anxiety" due to too few charging stations.   (191 words)

---

² emission [ɪmíʃ(ə)n]：排出   ² transport sector：輸送部門   ² account for ...：…を占める
³ petrol [pétr(ə)l]：ガソリン   ⁴ congestion [kəndʒéstʃ(ə)n]：混雑
⁶ sustainable [səstéɪnəb(ə)l]：持続可能な   ⁷ enact [ɪnǽkt]：…を制定する
⁷ greenhouse-gas：温室効果ガス   ¹² stem from ...：…から起こる   ¹⁴ sprawl [sprɔ́ːl]：広がり
¹⁴ transition [trænzíʃ(ə)n]：移行   ¹⁴ hinder [híndər]：…を妨げる   ¹⁵ potential [pəténʃ(ə)l]：潜在的な
¹⁶ range anxiety：走行距離不安

---

1. この英文のタイトルとして最も適当なものを、次の a.～d. から選びなさい。 （5点）

    a. Efforts to Cut CO_2 Emissions from Cars and the Present Situation

    b. Problems Caused by Design of Petrol Engine Cars

    c. Some Global Environmental Policies to Increase Electric Cars

    d. The Amounts of Greenhouse-Gases Emitted from Vehicles

精 読問題 もう一度英文を読んで、次の問いに答えなさい。

2. 下線部(1)について、例として挙げられているものを、本文中から３つ抜き出しなさい。 （各2点）

3. 下線部(2)が具体的に指しているものを、本文中から抜き出しなさい。 （3点）

4. 文法 下線部(3)の具体的な内容を日本語で説明しなさい。 （4点）

5. Ａ：下線部(4)は最終的に何の原因となりますか。第３パラグラフから６語で抜き出しなさい。

    （4点）

    Ｂ：また、下線部(4)はどのようにしてＡの原因となっていますか。日本語で説明しなさい。（8点）

6. 下線部(5)について、従来の自動車から電気自動車への移行を妨げている要因として、２つのことが挙げられています。この２つを日本語で答えなさい。 （各4点）

7. 全体把握 本文の内容と合っているものにはＴ、合っていないものにはＦと答えなさい。（各2点）

    (ア) About 24% of the global CO_2 emissions are from private cars. （　　　）

    (イ) Emission limits caused air pollution from vehicles. （　　　）

    (ウ) Car ownership in Europe in 2017 was 25% more than that in 2000. （　　　）

    (エ) People don't want to have electric cars due to their decreasing incomes.

    （　　　）

    (オ) Fewer electric cars are leading to fewer charging stations. （　　　）

Grammar 目標 ➡ 7分

1 ( )内の動詞を、現在完了形か過去完了形にしなさい。 (各2点)

1. We aren't hungry.　We (just have) lunch.　_____

2. We weren't hungry.　We (just have) lunch.　_____

3. The house is dirty.　They (not clean) it for weeks.　_____

4. The house was dirty.　They (not clean) it for weeks.　_____

5. Tommy is excited.　He (never see) snow before.　_____

6. Tommy was excited.　He (never see) snow before.　_____

2 下線部の動詞を過去形にして、全文を書きかえなさい。 (各3点)

1. Tom <u>says</u> that he is very angry.

   _____

2. Diana <u>thinks</u> that she will pass the test.

   _____

3. Mary <u>says</u> that she has found a good apartment.

   _____

4. Tom <u>insists</u> that he saw a UFO.

   _____

Writing 目標 ➡ 3分

3 ( )内に与えられた語を並べかえて、英文を完成しなさい。 (各4点)

1. きのうまで、そのことについては聞いたこともありませんでした。

   Until yesterday, I (about / had / heard / it / never).

   _____

2. ホールに着いたとき、コンサートはもう始まっていた。

   The concert (already / had / started / we / when) got to the hall.

   _____

3. ロバートは、このところアンを見かけていないと言いました。

   Robert said (Ann / hadn't / he / seen / that) recently.

   _____

CAN-DO List ☐ 🔍 〈知識・技能〉現在完了形、過去完了形、時制の一致を適切に活用することができる。

Listening

目標 → 5分　　テーマ ファッション　共通テスト　◀)) 11

4 英語を聞き、四つの空欄 1 ～ 4 に入れるのに最も適当なものを一つずつ選びなさい。

(各2点)

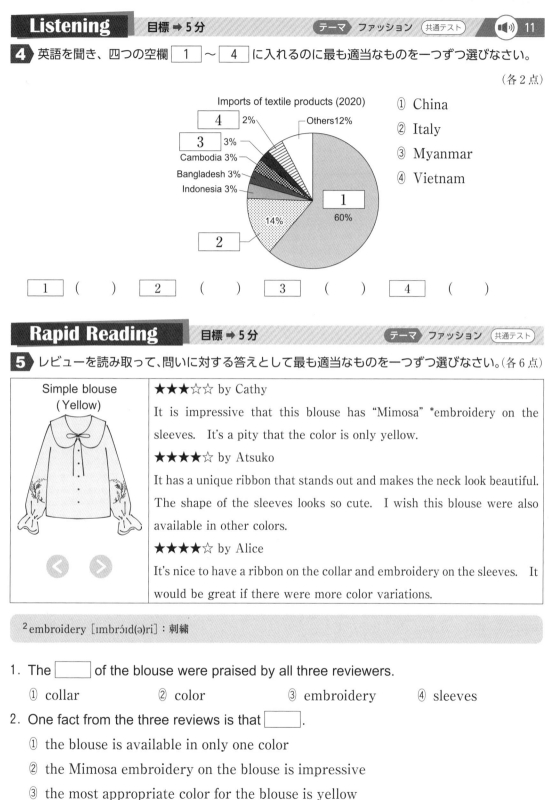

Imports of textile products (2020)

- 4 2%
- 3 3%
- Cambodia 3%
- Bangladesh 3%
- Indonesia 3%
- Others 12%
- 1 60%
- 2 14%

① China
② Italy
③ Myanmar
④ Vietnam

1 (　　)　　2 (　　)　　3 (　　)　　4 (　　)

Rapid Reading

目標 → 5分　　テーマ ファッション　共通テスト

5 レビューを読み取って、問いに対する答えとして最も適当なものを一つずつ選びなさい。(各6点)

Simple blouse
(Yellow)

★★★☆☆ by Cathy

It is impressive that this blouse has "Mimosa" *embroidery on the sleeves.　It's a pity that the color is only yellow.

★★★★☆ by Atsuko

It has a unique ribbon that stands out and makes the neck look beautiful. The shape of the sleeves looks so cute.　I wish this blouse were also available in other colors.

★★★★☆ by Alice

It's nice to have a ribbon on the collar and embroidery on the sleeves.　It would be great if there were more color variations.

² embroidery [ɪmbrɔ́ɪd(ə)ri]：刺繍

1. The ⬚ of the blouse were praised by all three reviewers.

　① collar　　　　② color　　　　③ embroidery　　　　④ sleeves

2. One fact from the three reviews is that ⬚ .

　① the blouse is available in only one color

　② the Mimosa embroidery on the blouse is impressive

　③ the most appropriate color for the blouse is yellow

　④ the pattern around the neck of the blouse is unique

速 読問題 次の英文を2.5分で読んで、1. の問いに答えなさい。

　The fashion industry needs to *fundamentally change in order to reduce the environmental impact of fast fashion, experts have said.　Clothes rental, better recycling processes, pollution control technology and the innovative use of *offcuts are among (1)steps that could help, they said.

5　The researchers produced a report on the environmental cost of the industry, and how (2)it needs to change to deal with some of the many associated problems.　While the figures are debated, the *Intergovernmental Panel on Climate Change (IPCC) has calculated the fashion industry produces 10% of global carbon dioxide emissions every year, while it is estimated to use around 1.5 trillion liters of water *annually.
10　*Meanwhile, there are many other problems, from chemical waste to microplastics.

　(3)Fast fashion is considered to be making the problems worse.　Cheap clothes are bought and thrown away *one after another as the fashion changes.　(4)"It is really a global problem," said Dr. Patsy Perry, a co-author of the research from Manchester University.

15　Perry and an international group of researchers point out that (5)the global *nature of the fashion industry means clothes may travel around the world several times during manufacture.　It is estimated that if 3% of *garment transportation *shifted from ships to airplanes, 100% more carbon dioxide could be emitted than if all garment transportation were by ships.

(218 words)

---

¹fundamentally [fÀndəmént(ə)li]：本質的に　　³offcut [ɔ́fkÀt]：切れ端
⁷Intergovernmental Panel on Climate Change：気候変動に関する政府間パネル
⁹annually [ǽnju(ə)li]：年間　　¹⁰meanwhile [míːn(h)wàɪl]：一方　　¹²one after another：次々に
¹⁵nature [néɪtʃər]：性質　　¹⁷garment [ɡɑ́ːrmənt]：衣服　　¹⁷shift [ʃíft]：…を変える

　CAN-DO List　□ 〈思考力・判断力・表現力〉時制の一致について理解できる。
　　　　　　　　　　□ 〈思考力・判断力・表現力〉ファッション業界と環境の関わりについて的確に理解できる。

1. この英文のタイトルとして最も適当なものを、次の a.〜d.から選びなさい。　　　　（5点）

   a. The Fashion Industry and Its Impact on the Environment

   b. How to Transport all Clothing

   c. The Intergovernmental Panel on Climate Change

   d. Trends in Fashion

精 読問題 もう一度英文を読んで、次の問いに答えなさい。

2. 下線部(1)の例として挙げられるものを表した箇所を、本文中から抜き出しなさい。　　（7点）

3. 下線部(2)が指すものを本文から抜き出しなさい。　　　　　　　　　　　　　　　　（5点）

4. 下線部(3)の理由を、日本語で説明しなさい。　　　　　　　　　　　　　　　　　　（7点）

5. 文法 次の文を完成させて、下線部(4)を引用符を用いない文に書きかえなさい。　　（6点）

Dr. Patsy Perry said that _____ .

6. 下線部(5)の説明として最も適当なものを、次の a.〜d.から選びなさい。　　　　　（4点）

   a. 衣服が出来上がるまでにくり返し輸出入されているという性質

   b. 多くの衣服が流行が過ぎたら捨てられてしまうという性質

   c. 衣服が安価であることが環境に大きな影響を与えているという性質

   d. 現状では衣服の輸出入は航空輸送に頼っているという性質

7. 全体把握 本文の内容と合っているものにはＴ、合っていないものにはＦと答えなさい。（各2点）

   (ア) The fashion industry needs to change in order to increase sales.　　（　　　）

   (イ) The innovative use of offcuts has nothing to do with the environment issues of the fashion industry.　　（　　　）

   (ウ) According to the Dr. Patsy Perry, the fashion industry produces 10% of global carbon dioxide emissions every year.　　（　　　）

   (エ) The fashion industry is also related to pollution problems, such as chemical waste and microplastics.　　（　　　）

   (オ) Changes in clothing fashions make pollution problem even worse.　　（　　　）

Lesson 5 助動詞

Grammar　目標 ➡ 7分

1 次の各文がほぼ同じ意味になるように、（　　）内に適語を補いなさい。　　(各3点)

1. You worked ten hours today.　I am sure you are tired.

   You worked ten hours today.　You (　　　　　　) be tired.

2. Take an umbrella with you.　Perhaps it will rain.

   Take an umbrella with you.　It (　　　　　　) rain.

3. It is possible that Sue will not come to the party.

   Sue (　　　　　　) not come to the party.

4. It is impossible that he is hungry because he has just had lunch.

   He has just had lunch.　He (　　　　　　) be hungry.

2 日本語に合うように、（　　）内に適当な語を補いなさい。　　(各3点)

1. [昼食を食べる場所を選んでいて] 「あのレストランはとてもいいにちがいないよ。」

   That restaurant (　　　　　　) be very good.　It's full of people.

2. [Where is Ken? と先生に聞かれて] 「彼はカフェにいるかもしれません。」

   I'm not sure.　He (　　　　　　) be in the cafeteria.

3. [うわさにおどろいて] 「それが本当であるはずがないよ。」

   I don't believe the rumor.　It (　　　　　　) be true.

Writing　目標 ➡ 5分

3 （　　）内に適語を補って、英文を完成しなさい。　　(各3点)

1. ここが私たちの探している場所にちがいない。

   This (　　　　　　) be the place we are looking (　　　　　　).

2. 今すぐ彼の申し出を受け入れなさい。あとになって彼は心変わりするかもしれませんよ。

   Accept his offer now.　He (　　　　　　) change his (　　　　　　) later.

3. もうこれ以上待たないことにしましょう。彼はやって来ないかもしれません。

   Let's not wait any longer.　He (　　　　　　) (　　　　　　) turn up.

4. あなたはきっと冗談を言っているのでしょう。本気のはずがありません。

   You (　　　　　　) be joking.　You (　　　　　　) be serious.

5. 彼は20代にちがいない。30歳を超えているはずはありません。

   He (　　　　　　) be in his twenties.　He (　　　　　　) be over 30.

CAN-DO List　□ 🔍 〈知識・技能〉推量を表す助動詞を適切に活用することができる。

4 対話とそれについての質問を聞き、答えとして最も適当なものを一つずつ選びなさい。　（各5点）

1. 母親が息子と玄関で話しています。

① 　② 　③ 　④

2. 父親が娘と動物園について話しています。

① 　② 　③ 　④

Rapid Reading 目標 ➡ 5分 　テーマ 家族 GTEC®

5 掲示を読み取って、問いに対する答えとして最も適当なものを一つずつ選びなさい。　（各5点）

Lost Cat
REWARD $50.00
"Tommy" the Kitten

Identifying marks : She has a heart shaped spot on her tail, one eye has a black spot and one eye is white.　She answers to her name.　She needs medicine right away.　Her family misses her very much.

Last seen : Fifth Street, New York on January 12th at 8：00 a.m.

Contact（XX）XXX-XXXX　**Email :** tommysfamily@daiichi.com

1. What should you do if you find Tommy？
　① Drive her to Fifth Street.　　② Give her medicine.
　③ Ask her what her name is.　　④ Call the number on the poster.

2. What is January 12th at 8：00 a.m. referring to？
　① A meeting time to find the cat.　　② The time and date the cat was last seen.
　③ A time and date to get the reward.　　④ A good time to call the family.

Reading　目標 → 20分　　文法項目　推量を表す助動詞　テーマ　家族　🔊 15

速読問題　次の英文を2.5分で読んで、1. の問いに答えなさい。

　　When I was in elementary school, I packed my suitcase and told my mother I was going to run away from home.　I *envisioned that I would live by a waterfall in the woods and catch fish on hooks made from the forks of tree *limbs, (1)as I had been taught by my father.　I would walk among the wildflowers and trees, listen to the birds, read

5　the weather report in the clouds and the wind, and stride down mountainsides independent and free.　(2)Wisely, my mother did not try to *dissuade me.　(3)She had been through this herself.　She checked my bag to see if I had my toothbrush and a postcard to let her know how I was getting along, and kissed me good-bye.　Forty minutes later I was home.

10　　When my daughter, Twig, was in elementary school, she told me she was going to run away to the woods.　I checked her backpack for her toothbrush and watched her go down the front steps, (4)her shoulders squared confidently.　I blew her a kiss and sat down to wait.　*Presently, she was back.

　　Although (5)wishing to run to the woods and live on our own must be an *inherited

15　characteristic in our family, we are not unique.　Almost everyone I know has dreamed at some time of running away to a distant mountain or island, castle or sailing ship, to live there in beauty and peace.　Few of us make it, however.　　　　　　　(243 words)

　CAN-DO List　　□ 💭 〈知識・技能〉推量を表す助動詞について理解できる。
　　　　　　　　　　　　　　　□ 💬 〈思考力・判断力・表現力〉家出に関するストーリーの展開を的確に理解することができる。

	Grammar	Writing	Listening	Rapid Reading	Reading	Total
	/21	/15	/10	/10	/44	/100

² envision [ɪnvíʒ(ə)n]：…を心に描く　　³ limb [lím]：枝
⁶ dissuade [dɪswéɪd]：…を説得して思いとどまらせる　　¹³ presently [préz(ə)ntli]：まもなく
¹⁴ inherit [ɪnhérət]：…を遺伝的に受け継ぐ

1. 子供のころ、家出をしようとしたことがある人をすべて選びなさい。　　　　（5点）

   a. the writer　　　　　　　　　　b. the writer's mother

   c. the writer's father　　　　　　　d. the writer's daughter

精 読問題 もう一度英文を読んで、次の問いに答えなさい。

2. 下線部(1)について、筆者が父親から教わったことは何ですか。日本語で説明しなさい。　（7点）

_____

_____

3. 下線部(2)について、筆者の母親が「賢明」であったことを証明した筆者自身の行動を表す箇所を本
  文中から6語で抜き出しなさい。　　　　　　　　　　　　　　　　　　（5点）

_____

4. 下線部(3)は具体的にどういうことですか。日本語で説明しなさい。　　　　（7点）

_____

5. 下線部(4)について、その解釈として最も適当なものを次のa.～d.から選びなさい。（4点）

   a. 意気消沈して肩を落として　　　　　b. 恐怖で肩が震えて

   c. 自信満々で胸を張って　　　　　　　d. 自分の計画を胸におさめて

6. 文法 筆者が下線部(5)のように思ったのはなぜですか。日本語で説明しなさい。　（6点）

_____

_____

7. 全体把握 本文の内容と合っているものにはT、合っていないものにはFと答えなさい。（各2点）

  (ア) The author and his family lived by a waterfall in the woods.　　（　　　）

  (イ) The author's father encouraged him to live on his own.　　　　（　　　）

  (ウ) The author's mother persuaded him to stay home.　　　　　　（　　　）

  (エ) Both the author and his daughter tried to run away from home.　（　　　）

  (オ) Almost everyone makes his or her dream of running away come true.（　　　）

Lesson 6 受動態

Grammar 目標 ➡ 7分

1 ( )内に下記の語群から適語を選び、過去分詞にして補いなさい。 (各2点)

1. I was ( ) some difficult questions at the interview.

2. The watch was ( ) to me for my 15th birthday.

3. A special meal was ( ) for the vegetarians.

4. A young dog is ( ) a puppy. A young cat is ( ) a kitten.

5. The gate was ( ) open all night.

【ask / call / cook / give / leave】

2 下線部を主語にした受動態の文を完成しなさい。(by ... は不要) (各3点)

1. We will discuss the problem at the meeting tomorrow.

   The problem will _____.

2. We can find a lot of wonderful people in the world.

   A lot of wonderful people can _____.

3. We must do something before it's too late.

   Something _____.

4. You should take this medicine three times a day.

   This medicine _____.

Writing 目標 ➡ 5分

3 ( )内に与えられた語句を並べかえて、英文を完成しなさい。 (各4点)

1. その子ネコはおなかをすかせていたので、ボール一杯のミルクが与えられました。

   The kitten was hungry, so (a bowl / given / it / of / was) milk.

   _____

2. エドは、チームでいちばんうまいプレーヤーだとみなされていました。

   Ed (considered / on / the best player / the team / was).

   _____

3. 空きビンを投げ捨ててはいけません。

   Empty bottles (away / be / must / not / thrown).

   _____

Listening

目標 ➡ 3分   テーマ お金   16～17

4 英語の質問と、それに対する応答が4つ読まれます。応答として最も適当なものを一つずつ選びなさい。 （各5点）

1. ①　　②　　③　　④

2. ①　　②　　③　　④

Rapid Reading

目標 ➡ 5分   テーマ お金   英検®

5 （1）・（2）に入るのに最も適当なものを、一つずつ選びなさい。 （各5点）

　　Money has not always been made of metal or paper. In many parts of the world people have used other materials. Precious stones, valuable cloth(silk), and rare spices have all been used as money at times. But people have also given special value to other kinds of objects. (1), in Ethiopia, blocks of salt have been used as money. In Malaysia, people have used large bronze drums. In India and in North America, special kinds of shells have been used. In fact, anything can become money (2).

1. ① As a result
   ② For example
   ③ However
   ④ Of course

2. ① if it has very little value
   ② if it is accepted by everyone as money
   ③ if it is easy for everyone to get
   ④ if it is easy to carry

Reading 　目標 ➡ 20分　　　文法項目 助動詞＋受動態　テーマ お金　　🔊 18

速 読問題 次の英文を2.5分で読んで、1. の問いに答えなさい。

　　To pay for things today, many people prefer to use credit cards because they are convenient.　For a child, credit cards must seem like magic because they allow a person to easily buy things.　In some countries, credit cards have become widely used quite recently, but in the United States they have been used for a long time.　The first

5　credit cards in the U.S. could only be used at gasoline stations when (1)they appeared in the 1920s.　In the 1950s, (2)"general purpose" credit cards appeared that could be used in many different kinds of stores.　At first, a person had to pay the *entire bill at the end of each month.　However, today, a customer can choose a payment plan so that they only need to pay a certain percentage of their charges.

10　　There is no question that credit cards are useful, but they have also caused many problems. One obvious problem is that people sometimes buy more than they can afford.　(3)This is especially a problem for college students who often *end up with credit card *debt.　Because the *interest (4)charged by credit card companies can be quite high, it is easy for the amount to build up quickly over a short period of time.

15　This problem becomes especially serious if a credit card is used too frequently.

(220 words)

---

⁷entire [ɪntáɪər]：全部の　　¹²end up with ...：ついには…で終わる　　¹³debt [dét]：借金、負債
¹³interest [ínt(ə)rəst]：利子、利息

　CAN-DO List　　□ 🔍 〈知識・技能〉助動詞＋受動態について理解できる。
　　　　　　　　　□ 📖 〈思考力・判断力・表現力〉クレジットカードの特徴について的確に理解できる。

1. この英文で主に述べられているものを、次のa.～d.から選びなさい。 （5点）

   a. 各種クレジットカードの比較

   b. クレジット会社の問題と課題

   c. クレジットカードの現状と将来のあり方

   d. クレジットカードの利便性と危険性

精 読問題 もう一度英文を読んで、次の問いに答えなさい。

2. 文法 下線部(1)について、次の質問に答えなさい。

   (A) they が指す内容を本文中から抜き出しなさい。 （5点）

_____

   (B) それらはどのような特徴がありましたか。日本語で説明しなさい。 （7点）

_____

3. 下線部(2)のクレジットカードを、日本語で簡単に説明しなさい。 （7点）

_____

4. 下線部(3)の This の具体的な内容を、日本語で説明しなさい。 （9点）

_____

_____

5. 下線部(4)の charged とほぼ同じ意味・内容の charge を含む文を、次のa.～d.から選びなさい。

（3点）

   a. He was charged with drunken driving.

   b. How much are they charging you for the repairs?

   c. I charged a new pair of shoes on my credit card.

   d. The bull put the head down and started to charge us.

6. 全体把握 本文の内容と合っているものにはT、合っていないものにはFと答えなさい。 （各2点）

   (ア) 子供にとっては、クレジットカードの仕組は理解しにくい。 （　　　　）

   (イ) かつて、月末には全てのつけが精算されなければならなかった。 （　　　　）

   (ウ) 大学生はみな、クレジットカードにつけをかかえ込むことになる。 （　　　　）

   (エ) クレジット会社は、短期間に大きな利益をあげることができる。 （　　　　）

   (オ) クレジットカードを頻繁に使いすぎるのは危険である。 （　　　　）

Lesson 7 to-不定詞①

Grammar 目標 ➡ 7分

1 （　　）内に、下の a.～ f.から適当なものを選び、記号を補いなさい。　　　　（各2点）

1. It is polite (　　　　　) when you ask for something.
2. Where's Bill?　He promised (　　　　　).
3. I have some jobs (　　　　　) before we go out.
4. I have no time (　　　　　) with the work.
5. Who was the first person (　　　　　) at the party?
6. It is necessary to have a license (　　　　　).

　a. to arrive　　　　　　　b. to be here on time　　　c. to do
　d. to drive a car　　　　　e. to help you　　　　　　　f. to say "Please"

2 （　　）内に下記の語群から適語を選んで補いなさい。　　　　　　　　　　（各2点）

1. We were (　　　　　) to know that the old man was still alive.
2. Thank you for your letter.　I was (　　　　　) to hear that you're doing well.
3. He isn't (　　　　　) to take his driving test.　He hasn't had enough lessons.
4. Do you think it's (　　　　　) to rain?
5. This is a room for students.　You're (　　　　　) to use this room.

　【free / glad / likely / ready / surprised】

Writing 目標 ➡ 5分

3 （　　）内に与えられた語句を並べかえて、英文を完成しなさい。　　　　（各4点）

1. 子供たちはすることがないと文句を言った。

　The children complained that (do / nothing / there / to / was).

　_____

2. 冬には、体を暖かくしておくためにコートを着ます。

　In winter we wear (coats / keep / our bodies / to / warm).

　_____

3. だれもが、何が起こったのか知りたがっていた。

　Everybody (anxious / know / to / was / what) had happened.

　_____

CAN-DO List　□　〈知識・技能〉to-不定詞の基本用法、be-動詞＋形容詞＋to-不定詞を適切に活用することができる。

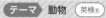
4 対話と質問を聞き、その答えとして最も適切なものを一つずつ選びなさい。 (各5点)

1. ① A puppy.　　　　　　　　　② A rabbit and a puppy.

　 ③ A rabbit and two tortoises.　④ Nothing.

2. ① Around the police station.　② In a cage.

　 ③ In a news program.　　　　④ Outside the zoo.

Rapid Reading 目標 ➡ 5分 テーマ 意見 GTEC®

5 レビューを読み取って、問いに対する答えとして最も適当なものを一つずつ選びなさい。(各5点)

The Maxon's All-in-one Printer PSC-3500w 	**Mr. T-bone （★★★☆☆）** The quality of the document printer is not bad considering its low price ($150.50 including tax). I'm not very satisfied with the photo printing, though. I think that's probably because it has only four-color ink cartridges. **RainGirl 2012 （★★★★☆）** I bought this printer mainly to print papers for my university classes. I had an old printer before, and the printing speed was too slow. But this model works much faster. Moreover, the maintenance cost is lower, I think. I can get ink cartridges for it at a pretty reasonable price on the Internet.

1. What aspect of the PSC-3500w does Mr. T-bone seem to be unhappy with?

　 ① Its price.

　 ② Its printing speed.

　 ③ The quality of its document printing.

　 ④ The quality of its photo printing.

2. On what aspect of the product do both users comment?

　 ① The cost of maintenance.　　② The design.

　 ③ The ink cartridges.　　　　　④ The photocopying function.

Reading　目標 ➡ 20分　｜文法項目｜ to-不定詞　｜テーマ｜ 動物　🔊 21

速読問題 次の英文を2.5分で読んで、1. の問いに答えなさい。

　There once was a man who traveled the world on a fine elephant.　One evening, he was looking for a place (1)to sleep and found a house where six brothers lived.　He knocked on the door and asked them to lend him a bed and some space for his elephant.　The brothers looked confused.　"What is an elephant?" they asked.　"You've never

5　seen one?" asked the man.　"You will be amazed!"　But it was already dark and there was no moon that night, so the man said, "(2)Let's sleep and I will show you the elephant in the morning."　The brothers smiled.　"We are all *blind," they told the man. "Please show us the thing that you call an elephant now.　We want to know all about it!"

　The man led the brothers to the elephant which was standing outside eating the

10　leaves of a tree, and the brothers stood around and began touching it.　However, the elephant was so big that every part being touched was different.　One brother touched its leg and said it was like the *pillar of a building.　Another brother held its tail and said it was like a thick rope.　A different brother touched its ear and said it felt like a leather *apron.

15　(3)The brothers began to fight about who was right.　After a little while, the man said, "Friends, there is no need to fight.　You are each right about the elephant.　But you are all wrong to think that you know the whole truth.　An elephant has many different parts.　(4)It's important for you to listen to your other brothers if you want to understand an elephant."

(276 words)

---

⁷ blind [bláɪnd]：目の見えない　¹² pillar [píləɾ]：柱　¹⁴ apron [éɪpr(ə)n]：エプロン

| CAN-DO List | □ 🔍 〈思考力・判断力・表現力〉to-不定詞について理解することができる。 |
| | □ 💡 〈思考力・判断力・表現力〉相互理解に関するストーリーの内容を的確に理解することができる。 |

1. この英文のタイトルとして最も適当なものを、次の a.～d. から選びなさい。 （5点）

   a. An Interesting Event in the Morning

   b. Blind Brothers Living in a House

   c. Brothers Who Touch an Elephant for the First Time

   d. Six Brothers Who Know a Lot about Elephants

精 読問題 もう一度英文を読んで、次の問いに答えなさい。

2. 文法 下線部(1)の to-不定詞と同じ用法の to-不定詞を含む文を本文中より抜き出しなさい。

（6点）

_____

3. 男は兄弟らになぜ下線部(2)のように言ったと考えられますか。日本語で説明しなさい。 （7点）

_____

4. 象の脚、尾、耳は何に例えられていますか。それぞれ本文中より抜き出しなさい。 （各2点）

   脚： _____

   尾： _____

   耳： _____

5. 下線部(3)について、空欄に適語を入れ、質問に対する答えを述べる文を完成させなさい。

（完答6点）

   Q：Why did the brothers begin to fight?

   A：Because they were all (　　　　　　　) and didn't know what a[an] (　　　　　　　) is
     like.

6. 下線部(4)について、兄弟の言うことを聞くというのは、具体的に何を聞くことだと考えられますか。
日本語で説明しなさい。 （6点）

_____

7. 全体把握 本文の内容と合っているものにはＴ、合っていないものにはＦと答えなさい。 （各2点）

   (ア) There were six people in a house, including a traveler. （　　　）

   (イ) The traveler was amazed because the elephant was very big. （　　　）

   (ウ) It was already dark when the man visited the brothers. （　　　）

   (エ) The elephant had to spend the night without eating anything. （　　　）

   (オ) Each brother had a different opinion about the elephant. （　　　）

Grammar 目標 ➡ 7分

1 例にならって、次の各文の内容を（　　）内の表現に続けなさい。　　　　（各3点）

例：Mary dropped her watch. （He saw ...）

→He saw Mary drop her watch.

1. He got into his car. （I saw ...）

_____

2. The clock struck twelve last night. （I heard ...）

_____

3. Something touched her cheek. （She felt ...）

_____

2 次の各文を、make [let]＋O＋動詞の原形（Oに～させる）の文に書きかえなさい。　（各3点）

1. A heavy rain caused us to cancel the picnic.

A heavy rain _____ the picnic.

2. The coach forced the team to practice for three hours every day.

The coach _____ for three hours every day.

3. Ann allowed me to use her computer.

Ann _____ her computer.

4. Please allow me to carry your bag for you.

Please _____ your bag for you.

Writing 目標 ➡ 3分

3 （　　）内に与えられた語句を並べかえて、英文を完成しなさい。　　　（各4点）

1. 私は眠っていたので、彼がドアをノックするのが聞こえなかった。

I was asleep and did not (knock / him / hear / the door / on).

_____

2. イヌがネコを追いかけているのを見た。　I (after / running / saw / the cat / the dog).

_____

3. きみを泣かせてしまってごめんなさい。　I'm (cry / I / made / sorry / you).

_____

CAN-DO List □ 🔍 〈知識・技能〉知覚動詞、使役動詞を適切に活用することができる。

4 長めの対話を一つ聞き、問いの答えとして最も適当なものを一つずつ選びなさい。 （各5点）

1. How much is a medium-sized coffee?

　① It is 50 cents.　② It is $1.00.　③ It is $1.50.　④ It is $2.00.

2. What did the man buy?

　① A black medium-sized coffee, a sandwich and a magazine.

　② A medium-sized coffee with cream, a sandwich and a newspaper.

　③ A black large-sized coffee, a sandwich and a newspaper.

　④ A large-sized coffee with cream, a sandwich and a newspaper.

Rapid Reading 目標 ➡ 5分 テーマ 仕事 英検®

5 （1）・（2）に入れるのに最も適当なものを一つずつ選びなさい。 （各5点）

　The first typewriters did not use the *present-day key *arrangement, but instead used a straight alphabetic design with keys *ordered from left to right and top to bottom. （　1　）, the printing parts often broke when a fast typist used the machine because the most *frequently used keys were too close together. To *correct this problem, an *inventor designed a different arrangement. It placed （　2　）.

---

¹present-day [préz(ə)nt-déɪ]：現代の、今日の　　　¹arrangement [əréɪn(d)ʒmənt]：配列、配置
²order [ɔ́ːrdər]：…を配列する　　　⁴frequently [fríːkwəntli]：しばしば、頻繁に
⁴correct [kərékt]：…を訂正する、正す　　　⁵inventor [ɪnvéntər]：発明した人

---

1. ① However　　② In addition　　③ In fact　　④ Instead

2. ① the keys in alphabetic order going from right to left and bottom to top

　② the keys in order of how frequently they are used

　③ the keys that are used most often far apart from each other

　④ the most frequently used keys next to each other

Reading 目標 ➡ 20分　文法項目 使役動詞　テーマ 仕事　🔊 23

速読問題 次の英文を 3 分で読んで、1. の問いに答えなさい。

　　The invention of canned coffee was *inspired by an *incident that happened in 1968. One day, a man named Tadao Ueshima, the owner of the Ueshima Coffee Company, was drinking *coffee-flavored milk at a train station.　In those days, if you drank a bottled drink, you had to return the bottle to the store after you finished it.　Mr. Ueshima's

5 train was leaving the station earlier than expected, so he did not have time to finish his drink.　He felt bad about wasting the milk, but (1)there was nothing he could do because he had to get back on the train.

　　He returned the bottle to the store with the unfinished milk and hurried onto the train at the last minute.　(2)This experience made Mr. Ueshima wonder if it would be

10 possible to make a coffee that people could drink anytime, anywhere.　The solution he *came up with was canned coffee.

　　By trial and error, Mr. Ueshima developed a technology for producing coffee drinks that could be put in a can without losing their flavor.　After a lot of hard work, Mr. Ueshima finally succeeded in producing the world's first canned coffee with milk

15 inside.

　　At first, the canned coffee did not sell as well as expected.　Perhaps it was because people were not accustomed to seeing coffee in a can.　However, at the 1970 World Exposition in Osaka, the canned coffee began to become popular.　After offering (3)free samples at the event, sales of canned coffee rapidly increased.

(249 words)

CAN-DO List □ 〈知識・技能〉使役動詞について理解できる。
□ 〈思考力・判断力・表現力〉缶コーヒーの誕生について的確に理解できる。

	Grammar	Writing	Listening	Rapid Reading	Reading	Total
	/21	/12	/10	/10	/47	/100

¹inspire [ɪnspáɪər]：…をもたらすきっかけとなる　　¹incident [ínsɪd(ə)nt]：(ちょっとした)出来事
³coffee-flavored：コーヒーの味がする　　¹¹come up with ...：(解決策など)を思いつく

1. この英文で主に述べられているものを、次の a.～d. から選びなさい。 （5点）

    a. あるコーヒー飲料会社の発展の歴史　　　b. 缶コーヒー誕生のいきさつ

    c. 新製品が誕生するまでの努力と苦労　　　d. 世界初の缶コーヒーに対する人々の反応

精 読問題 もう一度英文を読んで、次の問いに答えなさい。

2. 下線部(1)について、なぜウエシマ氏は牛乳をむだにしてしまったのですか。日本語で説明しなさい。

（10点）

_____

3. **文法** 下線部(2)について、次の問いに答えなさい。

    (A) This experience の内容を日本語で説明しなさい。 （10点）

_____

    (B) 下線部(2)の結果生まれた商品を本文中から2語で抜き出しなさい。 （4点）

    (　　　　　) (　　　　　　　)

4. 下線部(3)の free とほぼ同じ意味の free を含む文を、次の a.～d. から選びなさい。 （4点）

    a. After six years in prison, at last he was <u>free</u>.

    b. Children under five usually travel <u>free</u> on trains.

    c. I'm <u>free</u> every evening this week.

    d. In a <u>free</u> society, you can say what you like about the government.

5. **全体把握** 本文の内容と合っているものにはT、合っていないものにはFと答えなさい。（各2点）

    (ア) One day, Tadao Ueshima was drinking coffee with milk at a coffee shop in a train station. (　　　)

    (イ) He was drinking a bottle of milk flavored with coffee at a station. (　　　)

    (ウ) His train left the station before he got back on it. (　　　)

    (エ) He returned the bottle of milk to the store after he finished it. (　　　)

    (オ) He thought canned coffee would help people to enjoy coffee anytime, anywhere.

    (　　　)

    (カ) His canned coffee was the world's first canned coffee with milk inside.

    (　　　)

    (キ) People were familiar with coffee in a can, so sales of canned coffee rapidly increased. (　　　)

Lesson 9 動名詞

Grammar 目標 ➡ 7分

1 ___ に下記の語群から適語を選び、〜ing 形か to 〜の形にして補いなさい。 (各2点)

1. Have you finished _____ your room?

2. Do you enjoy _____ other countries?

3. Mary suggested _____ dinner at a restaurant.

4. Karen failed _____ a good impression at the job interview.

5. Sarah gave up _____ to find a job in this country and decided _____ abroad.

【clean / go / have / make / try / visit】

2 ▢ 内から適当なものを選び、___ に前置詞＋動名詞の表現を補いなさい。 (各2点)

| by / for / from / of / without | ＋ | get / do / lock / stand / wait |

1. I'm tired _____ the same thing every day.

2. Sorry I'm late! Thank you _____.

3. I went out _____ the door.

4. I was able to reach the top shelf _____ on a chair.

5. My bad cold prevented me _____ out of bed yesterday.

Writing 目標 ➡ 5分

3 ( )内に適語を補って、英文を完成しなさい。 (各3点)

1. 雨がやむまでは外出しません。

   I'm not going out until (   ) stops (   ).

2. 天気がよかったので、私は川辺に散歩に行きましょうと言った。

   The weather was nice, so I (   ) (   ) for a walk by the river.

3. 慎重に運転することで、事故を避けることができます。

   (   ) (   ) carefully, you can avoid accidents.

4. 留守中庭の世話をしてくださってありがとうございました。

   Thank you (   ) (   ) care of the garden while I was away.

5. 私たちはついにすてきなアパートを見つけることができました。

   We've finally succeeded (   ) (   ) a nice apartment.

CAN-DO List ☐ 🔍 〈知識・技能〉S＋V＋O (to-不定詞 / 動名詞)、前置詞＋動名詞を適切に活用することができる。

4 それぞれのイラストについて対話を聞き、最後の発言に対する相手の応答として最も適当なものを一つずつ選びなさい。 (各5点)

1.  ① ② ③ ④

2. ① ② ③ ④

Rapid Reading　目標 ➡ 5分　　テーマ　レストラン　GTEC®

5 メニューを読み取って、問いに対する答えとして最も適当なものを一つずつ選びなさい。(各5点)

Menu
Italian Dining & Café

Starters	Pizza (12 inch)	Pasta
Soup	Beef, Mushroom & Onion Pizza	Shrimp Spaghetti ------ $26.00
Chicken Soup ---------- $12.50	----------------------- $15.00	Super Seafood Spaghetti
Mushroom Soup ------- $12.50	Chicken & Pork Pizza - $14.50	----------------------- $26.00
Salad	Vegetarian Pizza ------- $14.00	Chicken Spaghetti ----- $25.50
Smoked Salmon Salad - $18.50	*You can add toppings for 50 ¢ each.*	Cold Drinks
Shrimp & Fresh Fruit Salad	**Burger**	Coke ----------------- $3.50
----------------------- $20.50	Cheese Burger ---------- $14.50	Orange Juice ----------- $5.00
Main Course	*Add bacon or egg ------- $1.00 each*	Dessert
Sandwiches	*Add avocado ------------ $1.50*	Today's Special Dessert
Ham & Cheese Sandwich		----------------------- $8.50
----------------------- $15.50		
Tuna & Egg Salad Sandwich		*Only soup, sandwiches and salads available at lunchtime.*
----------------------- $16.00		

1. How much would it cost to add chicken and mushroom to a 12 inch pizza?
   ① 50 cents ② $1.00
   ③ $1.50 ④ $2.00

2. When are pizza and pasta available?
   ① Dinner time only. ② Lunchtime only.
   ③ Both dinner and lunchtime. ④ Neither dinner or lunchtime.

Reading　目標 ➡ 20分　　文法項目 動名詞　テーマ レストラン　 26

速|読問題 次の英文を2.5分で読んで、1. の問いに答えなさい。

In the summer of 1853, George Crum was working at a small restaurant in New York. One day, a customer appeared who didn't like (1)George's French-fried potatoes. That customer changed George's life then and there.

The waiter went into the kitchen to talk with George. "One of the customers says
5 that these French-fried potatoes are too thick. Please make some thinner ones," the waiter said.

George (2)was upset to hear that the customer was complaining. But *the customer is always right. So, George took some potatoes, sliced them thinner than before, fried them, and sent them out to the customer. Again the customer complained that they
10 were too thick.

When George heard that the customer was still complaining, (3)he became very angry. George thought, "Sending things back to the kitchen once is understandable, but sending the fried potatoes back a second time is too rude." Then George took out some potatoes and sliced them as thin as paper to get *revenge on the customer. "He'll be
15 surprised to see these fried potatoes. He won't even be able to use his fork," George laughed.

When he finished frying the potatoes, they were not like the thick soft fried potatoes which he always made. They were hard and brown. George smiled and was pleased with (4)his "revenge." He then sent them out to the customer.

20 The customer, however, was not angry to see the *crispy potatoes. In fact, he ate them happily. George Crum's "revenge" on that one customer became (5)one of the best-selling snacks of all time everywhere. Do you know what it is? (263 words)

CAN-DO List
□ 〈知識・技能〉動名詞について理解できる。
□ 〈思考力・判断力・表現力〉レストランで起こった出来事について的確に理解できる。

[7] the customer is always right：お客様は神さまです（当時の接客業者のモットー）
[14] revenge [rivén(d)ʒ]：仕返し、報復　　[20] crispy [kríspi]：カリカリ[パリパリ]とした

1. この英文のタイトルとして最も適当なものを、次の a.〜d. から選びなさい。　　　　（5点）

　　a. 痛ましい報復の連鎖　　　　　　　　b. クレームから生まれたヒット商品

　　c. 誇り高き料理人　　　　　　　　　　d. レストランのわがままなお客

精 読問題 もう一度英文を読んで、次の問いに答えなさい。

2. 下線部(1)はどのようなものでしたか。ほぼ同じ内容を表している箇所を本文中から抜き出しなさ

　　い。　　　　　　　　　　　　　　　　　　　　　　　　　　　　　　　　　　（5点）

_____

3. 下線部(2)の意味として最も適当なものを、次の a.〜d. から選びなさい。　　　　（3点）

　　a. 落ち込んだ　　　　b. 悲しんだ　　　　c. 思い悩んだ　　　　d. 腹をたてた

4. 文法 下線部(3)について、ジョージを怒らせたお客の行動を表す箇所を本文中から8語で抜き出

　　しなさい。　　　　　　　　　　　　　　　　　　　　　　　　　　　　　　　（7点）

_____

5. 下線部(4)の具体的な内容を、日本語で説明しなさい。　　　　　　　　　　　　（7点）

_____
_____

6. 下線部(5)は何ですか。日本語で簡潔に答えなさい。　　　　　　　　　　　　　（6点）

_____

7. 全体把握 本文の内容と合っているものにはT、合っていないものにはFと答えなさい。（各2点）

　　(ア) The customer complained that George's French-fried potatoes were too hard.

　　　　　　　　　　　　　　　　　　　　　　　　　　　　　　　　（　　　　）

　　(イ) At first, George thought he should always show respect to customers even if they

　　　　were unreasonable or unpleasant.　　　　　　　　　　　　　（　　　　）

　　(ウ) George got very angry when he talked with the customer.　　　（　　　　）

　　(エ) George fried potatoes three times for the customer.　　　　　　（　　　　）

　　(オ) The customer liked George's French-fried potatoes because they were thick and

　　　　soft.　　　　　　　　　　　　　　　　　　　　　　　　　　（　　　　）

　　(カ) The snacks which were first made by George Crum are very popular now.

　　　　　　　　　　　　　　　　　　　　　　　　　　　　　　　　（　　　　）

Lesson 10 分詞

Grammar 目標 ➡ 7分

1 ( )内に下記の語群から適語を選び、現在分詞か過去分詞にして補いなさい。 (各2点)

1. He lay on his back ( ) at the sky.

2. The old lady sat ( ) by her grandchildren.

3. I saw the boys ( ) stones at the fruit on the tree.

4. Didn't you hear your name ( )?

5. We went into the house and found him ( ) on the floor.

6. We usually keep the front door ( ).

【call / lie / lock / look / surround / throw】

2 例にならって、一つの文[分詞構文の文]を作りなさい。 (各3点)

例：She heard the doorbell. She ran to open the door.
　　→Hearing the doorbell, she ran to open the door.

1. She waved her hand. She smiled at me.

_____

2. "Don't worry," she said. She laid her hand on my shoulder.

_____

3. The tree was removed from the garden. It left a big hole.

_____

Writing 目標 ➡ 3分

3 ( )内に与えられた語句を並べかえて、英文を完成しなさい。 (各4点)

1. 宇宙飛行士たちには、地球がさながら青い球体のように宇宙空間に浮かんでいるのが見えた。

The astronauts could see (hanging / in / like / space / the earth) a blue globe.

_____

2. この話はもう何度も何度も聞かされました。

I (have / heard / repeated / this story / too) often.

_____

3. お待たせしてすみません。

I'm (I've / kept / sorry / waiting / you).

_____

CAN-DO List ☐ 🔍 〈知識・技能〉S＋V＋C（分詞）、S＋V＋O＋C（分詞）、分詞構文を適切に活用することができる。

4 長めの対話を一つ聞き、問いの答えとして最も適当なものを一つずつ選びなさい。 （各5点）

1. Which of the following will the girl NOT join on the sports day?

  ① Marching.   ② Dancing.

  ③ 200-meter relay race.   ④ 800-meter relay race.

2. When does the girl practice running?

  ① This Sunday.   ② Before the class starts.

  ③ During the lunch break.   ④ After school.

Rapid Reading 目標 ➡ 5分 テーマ 家族

5 投稿を読み取って、（1）・（2）に入れるのに最も適当なものを一つずつ選びなさい。 （各5点）

 Andy's dad
2 hrs ago

    Thank you so much everyone for your wonderful gifts for my son and fun yesterday. My son Andy had a wonderful time on the 21st of April celebrating his 10th Birthday. He started off with 2 bowling games at Bowl Center. He played with 6 of his friends. Then we all went to our house for a pizza, chips and ice cream cake, singing happy birthday.

    Andy finished his birthday （ 1 ） visit from his grandpa and grandma from Canada. He was so happy to see them as it had been about 2 years since we last （ 2 ） them.

👍 good !   💬 comment

1. ① with a surprised ② with a surprising ③ with surprised ④ with surprising

2. ① looked   ② saw   ③ see   ④ watched

Reading 目標➡20分 文法項目 分詞構文 テーマ 家族 28

速読問題 次の英文を2.5分で読んで、1. の問いに答えなさい。

My mom grew up in a traditional Chinese family.　Open expressions of love were never encouraged in the family.　When she had me and my three brothers, (1)she treated us with the same hard hand.　She was not too severe, but she never openly showed affection.　Instead, she showed that she cared in more practical ways.

5　On the other hand, my dad was a really open-hearted person who constantly showered us with hugs and kisses.　After much persuasion from my dad, my mother did try to change, but it was clear that she never felt quite right in expressing her emotions.　(2)Eventually she went back to her old self.

The difference between my parents was never more *stark than when I brought

10　home good test results from school.　(3)My dad would practically jump for joy, offering warm and affectionate words of congratulations.　And my mother？　"Ah, good, good," she would typically say with a *tense smile on her face.　"Do better next time, OK？" She was so (4)reserved.　That was just her way.

We children secretly *yearned for her kisses.　(5)We received a quick, light kiss on

15　the cheek from her once a year on Chinese New Year when she gave us our *ang pow (red packet for money).　I can remember the kisses, awkward and wet, from her *Dior lipstick.　We would *rub the mark on our cheek, trying to look displeased.　But we were secretly glad to get a kiss from our mom.

(245 words)

⁹stark [stάːrk]：(違いが)きわだった　　¹²tense [téns]：こわばった　　¹⁴yearn [jə́ːrn]：待ち望む、切望する
¹⁵ang pow：紅包(日本のお年玉にあたるもの)　　¹⁶Dior lipstick：ディオールの口紅　　¹⁷rub [rΛb]：…をこする

CAN-DO List ☐ 〈知識・技能〉分詞構文について理解できる。
☐ 〈思考力・判断力・表現力〉登場人物の性格について的確に理解できる。

1. この英文に出てくる母親の姿として最も適当なものを、次の a.～ d. から選びなさい。　　（5点）

　　a. いつも子供たちを支え、励ましてくれた母親

　　b. 子供たちの成長を静かに見守ってくれた母親

　　c. 表現は控えめであったが、子供たちをじゅうぶんに愛してくれた母親

　　d. 古くからのしきたりを厳格に守り続けた母親

精 読問題 もう一度英文を読んで、次の問いに答えなさい。

2. 下線部(1)は具体的にどういうことですか。日本語で説明しなさい。　　（8点）

_____

3. 下線部(2)は具体的にどういうことですか。日本語で説明しなさい。　　（7点）

_____

_____

4. **文法** 次の文が下線部(3)とほぼ同じ意味になるように、下記の語群から適語を選んで（　　）内に補いなさい。　　（6点）

　　My dad would practically jump for joy, (　　　　) he would offer warm and affectionate words of congratulations.

　　【and / because / if / but】

5. 下線部(4)の reserved とほぼ反対の意味で使われている語を、本文中から抜き出しなさい。

_____　　（4点）

6. 下線部(5)について、母親からキスをされたときの子供たちの示した反応と心情を日本語で説明しなさい。　　（9点）

_____

_____

7. **全体把握** 次の英文の ☐ に入れるのに最も適当なものを、それぞれ下の a.～ c. から一つずつ選びなさい。　　（各4点）

　(ア) My mom never openly showed affection because ☐ .

　　a. she cared in more practical ways

　　b. she had grown up in a traditional Chinese family

　　c. my father had persuaded her not to do so

　(イ) We would rub the kiss mark on our cheek because ☐ .

　　a. the kiss was awkward and wet

　　b. we were displeased but we wanted to look glad

　　c. we wanted to look displeased though we were glad

Grammar 目標 ⇒ 7分

1 ＿＿に下記の語群から適語を選び、必要に応じて形を変えて補いなさい。 (各2点)

1. How fast you're growing! You'll soon be as ＿＿＿＿＿＿＿＿＿＿ as your father.

2. The hotel was ＿＿＿＿＿＿＿＿＿＿ than I expected.

3. His illness was ＿＿＿＿＿＿＿＿＿＿ than the doctor first thought.

4. The population of Italy is about half as ＿＿＿＿＿＿＿＿＿＿ as that of Japan.

5. He has twice as ＿＿＿＿＿＿＿＿＿＿ books as I do.

【large / many / serious / small / tall】

2 次の各文がほぼ同じ意味になるように、( )内に適語を補いなさい。 (各2点)

1. The viola is not as small as the violin.

   The violin is ( ) ( ) the viola.

2. Light travels faster than sound.

   Sound doesn't travel ( ) ( ) ( ) light.

3. Our hotel was cheaper than all the others in the town.

   We stayed at ( ) ( ) hotel in the town.

4. The USA is about one-third as large as Africa.

   Africa is about ( ) ( ) as large as the USA.

Writing 目標 ⇒ 3分

3 ( )内に与えられた語句を並べかえて、英文を完成しなさい。 (各4点)

1. 彼らはここに、私たちほど長くは暮らしていません。

   They haven't (as / as / here / lived / long) we have.

   ＿＿＿＿＿＿＿＿＿＿＿＿＿＿＿＿＿＿＿＿＿＿＿＿＿＿＿＿＿＿＿＿＿

2. 私たちの先生は実際の年齢よりも若く見えます。

   Our teacher (he really / is / looks / than / younger).

   ＿＿＿＿＿＿＿＿＿＿＿＿＿＿＿＿＿＿＿＿＿＿＿＿＿＿＿＿＿＿＿＿＿

3. 彼女は本当にいい人です。私が知っている中で最もいい人の一人です。

   She is a really nice person —— (I / know / of / one / people / the nicest).

   ＿＿＿＿＿＿＿＿＿＿＿＿＿＿＿＿＿＿＿＿＿＿＿＿＿＿＿＿＿＿＿＿＿

4 英文と質問を聞き、その答えとして最も適当なものを一つずつ選びなさい。 (各5点)

1. ① It offers students the opportunity to improve the operating ability of computers.

   ② It offers students the opportunity to learn internationally.

   ③ It offers students the opportunity to make friends with foreigners.

   ④ It offers students the opportunity to study abroad.

2. ① It is the ability to calculate by using a computer.

   ② It is the basic ability to make computers.

   ③ It is the basic ability to read and write sentences.

   ④ It is the basic ability to use a computer.

Rapid Reading 目標 ➡ 5分 テーマ 情報化社会

5 記事を読み取って、問いに対する答えとして最も適当なものを一つずつ選びなさい。 (各5点)

Phones to prevent *fraud selling well

We have to be careful about fraud. More than 80% of victims are seniors aged 60 and over. According to experts, the key to preventing this kind of fraud is the telephone, because it is the first point of contact with the *criminal. Therefore, phones with a function to prevent fraud are gradually becoming widespread. One of them is a new phone with a warning function. It tells the caller that the call will be recorded before the phone rings. A person who is trying to *commit a crime will *hang up upon hearing this. If the person hangs up, the call will not connect, of course.

¹ fraud [frɔ́ːd]：詐欺　⁴ criminal [krímɪn(ə)l]：犯人
⁶ commit a crime：罪を犯す　⁷ hang up：電話を切る

1. Who are the main victims of fraud?

   ① People who are not cautious are.

   ② People who don't have new telephones are.

   ③ Senior people aged 60 and over are.　④ Young people are.

2. How does a phone with a warning function work?

   ① It displays the caller's phone number.

   ② It does not accept calls from any number other than registered ones.

   ③ It tells the caller that the call will be recorded.

   ④ When the phone rings, it tells us that the caller may be a criminal.

16 PEACE, JUSTICE AND STRONG INSTITUTIONS

Reading

目標 ➡20分　　文法項目 比較　テーマ 情報化社会　◀)) 31

速読問題 次の英文を2.5分で読んで、1. の問いに答えなさい。

　　Today we are at *the Newseum in Washington, D.C. — where the history of free expression is explained and defended.　The first printing presses arrived in the United States in the mid-1600s and marked an important step in the history of America's *free press.

5　　A free press is important in a *democratic society.　(1)It allows citizens to speak freely and criticize the country's leaders without fear.　Some journalists have even lost their lives for that right.　But it can also lead to news that is false.　Last year, a fake news story about a Washington pizza restaurant spread, and a gunman *opened fire on the restaurant.

10　　One of the most common terms we hear today is "fake news."　The public and politicians use (2)the term to talk about the news reports they do not think are accurate.　While people have paid much attention to the term in recent years, the problem is not new.　False news reports have been around since modern journalism started.

　　Today, information moves around us in many forms, every hour of every day.　Even
15　if we do not seek out news on our own, we often receive it anyway, instantly, on our phones.　So how can we manage this mountain of information so that fake news does not mislead us?　We believe (3)this requires news literacy.　(4)News literacy is the ability to use critical thinking skills to judge news reports.　Are they *credible?　Can you rely on the reports to be true?

20　　The need for news literacy is possibly (5)greater now than ever before.　Learning this important skill can give us the power to take full control of our own search for the truth.　Because as we've seen many times before, some news presented as truth can actually

CAN-DO List
☐ 🔍 〈知識・技能〉比較について理解できる。
☐ 💭 〈思考力・判断力・表現力〉リテラシーの重要性について的確に理解できる。

turn out to be completely false.

(297 words)

¹the Newseum：ニュージアム（ワシントン D.C. にあった報道に関する資料を収集・展示する博物館）
³free press：報道の自由　　⁵democratic [dèməkrǽtɪk]：民主主義の　　⁸open fire on ...：…に発砲する
¹⁸credible [krédəb(ə)l]：信頼できる

1. 作者の主張を表したものを、次の a.〜d. から選びなさい。 (5点)

   a. Almost all news today is fake news, so we should not be easily deceived.

   b. Learning news literacy will help you determine what is true.

   c. News literacy is more difficult to learn than before.

   d. You are more likely to understand news clearly by learning news literacy.

精 読問題 もう一度英文を読んで、次の問いに答えなさい。

2. 下線部(1)が指すものを、本文中から抜き出しなさい。 (7点)

3. 下線部(2)が指すものを、本文中から抜き出しなさい。 (7点)

4. 下線部(3)は具体的には何のことですか。日本語で説明しなさい。 (8点)

5. 下線部(4)について、次の英文の □ に入れるのに最も適当なものを、a.〜c. から選びなさい。

(5点)

People with news literacy □ .

   a. try to research the influence of fake news

   b. read the news carefully and think whether it is reliable or not

   c. don't look for as much news as possible on their smartphones

6. 文法 下線部(5)は何と何を比べているか。日本語で答えなさい。 (8点)

_____ と _____

7. 全体把握 本文の内容と合っているものには T、合っていないものには F と答えなさい。 (各2点)

  (ア) Newseum exhibits the history of the United States. (　　)

  (イ) Some journalists have lost their lives for the right of a free press. (　　)

  (ウ) The fake news problem is a new problem that did not exist in the past. (　　)

  (エ) Modern people may receive a variety of information even if they don't ask for it.

(　　)

  (オ) You need to learn news literacy to seek the truth for yourself. (　　)

Lesson 12 接続詞

Grammar 目標 ➡ 7分

1 ( )内に、下記の語群から適語を選んで補いなさい。 (各2点)

1. It is strange ( ) he is not here. He always comes at this time.
2. The manager asked me ( ) I had a driver's license.
3. The problem is ( ) I don't have any money right now.
4. Does the Bible really explain ( ) life means?

【if / that / that / what】

2 ( )内に、下記の語群から適語を選んで補いなさい。 (各2点)

1. We're going to play tennis ( ) it doesn't rain.
2. I'm going away for a few days. I'll call you ( ) I get back.
3. She accepted the job ( ) the salary was rather low.
4. I love New York, but I wouldn't like to live there ( ) it's too big.
5. Don't go out yet. Wait ( ) the rain stops.
6. Open the door ( ) the cat can go out.
7. I was so tired ( ) I fell asleep in the armchair.

【although / because / if / so that / that / until / when】

Writing 目標 ➡ 3分

3 ( )内に適語を補って、英文を完成しなさい。 (各3点)

1. 彼らが日本でのコンサートを中止したのは残念です。

   ( ) is a pity ( ) they have canceled their concert in Japan.

2. 今日は雨になるのかしら。

   I ( ) ( ) it will rain today.

3. 手遅れにならないうちに何か手をうつべきだ。

   We should do something ( ) it is ( ) late.

4. 彼は10歳になってやっと泳げるようになった。

   He ( ) learn to swim ( ) he was ten.

5. レストランは混雑していたけれど、私たちはテーブルを確保することができた。

   We were ( ) to find a table ( ) the restaurant was crowded.

6. 彼の足はとても大きいので、合う靴を見つけるのがむずかしい。

   His feet are ( ) big that it's difficult ( ) him to find shoes.

CAN-DO List ☐ 〈知識・技能〉名詞節を導く接続詞、副詞節を導く接続詞を適切に活用することができる。

Listening

目標 ➡ 5分　　　　　　　　　　　　テーマ 旅行　 32

4 長めの英文を一つ聞き、問いの答えとして最も適当なものを一つずつ選びなさい。　(各5点)

1. When did the tower begin to lean?

① Just 5 years after the tower started to be built.

② When the top of the tower was completed.

③ About 200 years after the tower started to be built.

④ In 1990.

2. Which is the best way to enter the tower?

① Arrive early in the morning.

② Get a ticket on the same day.

③ Enter without permission.

④ Make a reservation online.

Rapid Reading

目標 ➡ 5分　　　　　　　　　　　　テーマ 旅行　GTEC®

5 ウェブサイトを読み取って、問いに対する答えとして最も適当なものを一つずつ選びなさい。

(各5点)

Visit South Africa				
	About South Africa	Tours	News	Contact

Language : English / 中文 / 日本語

In South Africa, travel companies provide visitors with a variety of tours to meet wildlife.

<An Eco-tour of Kruger National Park>
We will give you a chance to see wild animals such as lions, elephants, and buffaloes when you move across the park. Also, you can join tours to see wild birds.

<A Tour of Boulders Beach>
Believe it or not, you can even see wild penguins in South Africa. You can see them living in their natural environment. We don't think you will find any other such places in the world.

Those eco-tours will give you unusual experiences and teach you the importance of protecting the natural environment.

1. In which tour can visitors probably see wild elephants?

① Both of the tours on the website.

② Neither of the tours on the website.

③ The one to Boulders Beach.

④ The one to Kruger National Park.

2. What will visitors to Boulders Beach get?

① Chances to see many kinds of animals.

② How to protect the natural environment.

③ Some unique experiences.

④ Wild penguins.

速読問題 次の英文を2.5分で読んで、1. の問いに答えなさい。

This is a short history of Mr. Lars-Eric Lindblad, a world-famous tour manager and *nature conservationist.　He was born in Sweden in 1927 and was brought up there. When he was a child, he was interested in unknown *exotic places and great explorers that he read about in books.　After he graduated from a university in Switzerland, he

5　moved to the United States in 1951.　It was when he was twenty-four years old.

He worked at travel companies for several years and then opened his own company in New York City in 1958.　However, it was different from other travel companies.　He began a new type of exciting tours with his creative mind.　He took his tour groups to *Antarctica.　Nobody had done this before.　In the following year, he took his group to

10　*the Galapagos Islands.　(1)This was also the first time in the world for tourists to visit the islands.　In 1967, he landed on *Easter Island with his tourists for the first time. After this, he began *commercial trips to China, to African countries, to the Amazon, for example.　Also, Mr. Lindblad thought of a unique idea.　He gave classes for the travelers to know about their *destinations.　In other words, his tourists could have fun

15　and learn at the same time.

Mr. Lindblad also believed (2)that travel companies should try to protect the natural environment because it was quite important for them.　For this goal, (3)he even bought two islands in *the Seychelles to protect their natural environment.　He died while he was on vacation in Sweden in 1994.　In 1993, his wife, Mrs. Ruriko Hosaka Lindblad,

20　started working as an *interpreter and a guide with tour groups.　Today she meets many tourists visiting these places each year.

(292 words)

---

²nature conservationist：自然保護活動家　　³exotic [ɪgzá(:)tɪk]：めずらしい

⁹Antarctica [æntáːrktɪkə]：南極大陸　　¹⁰the Galapagos Islands：ガラパゴス諸島

¹¹Easter Island：イースター島　　¹²commercial [kəmə́ːrʃ(ə)l]：商業的な

¹⁴destination [dèstɪnéɪʃ(ə)n]：目的地　　¹⁸the Seychelles：セーシェル諸島

²⁰interpreter [ɪntə́ːrprətər]：通訳

CAN-DO List ☐ 〈知識・技能〉接続詞の that について理解できる。
☐ 〈思考力・判断力・表現力〉リンドブラッド氏に関するストーリーの展開を的確に理解することができる。

1. この英文のタイトルとして最も適当なものを、次の a.〜d. から選びなさい。　　　（5点）

    a. How to Protect the Natural Environment

    b. Mr. Lindblad's First Trip to the Galapagos Islands

    c. The Life of Mr. Lindblad

    d. The Role of Travel Companies in the Environment

精 読問題 もう一度英文を読んで、次の問いに答えなさい。

2. 次の英文の空欄に入る地名を、本文中より抜き出しなさい。　　　（完答6点）

    Mr. Lindblad came from ＿＿＿＿＿＿＿＿. He began to live in ＿＿＿＿＿＿＿＿

    after he graduated from university in ＿＿＿＿＿＿＿.

3. 下線部(1)の具体的な内容を、日本語で説明しなさい。　　　（7点）

_____

4. 文法 下線部(2)の that と同じ用法の that が用いられている文を、次の a.〜c. から選びなさい。

    　　　（3点）

    a. I told my mother that she should take a rest.

    b. The news that Takeshi could not join the trip disappointed us.

    c. This is the best book that I have ever read.

5. 下線部(3)の理由を、日本語で説明しなさい。　　　（7点）

_____

6. 次の質問に対する答えとして適切なものを下の a.〜d. から選びなさい。　　　（4点）

    When did Mrs. Ruriko Hosaka Lindblad begin her work as an interpreter and a guide?

    a. A year before Mr. Lindblad died.

    b. Only after Mr. Lindblad died.

    c. When Mr. Lindblad started his own company.

    d. When she married Mr. Lindblad.

7. 全体把握 本文の内容と合っているものにはＴ、合っていないものにはＦと答えなさい。（各2点）

    (ア) When Mr. Lindblad was a child, he was interested in writing stories about famous

        explorers.　　　　　　　　　　　　　　　　　　　　　　　　（　　）

    (イ) Mr. Lindblad went to a university in his home country.　　　　　（　　）

    (ウ) Mr. Lindblad began commercial trips to China after he landed on Easter Island

        with his tourists for the first time.　　　　　　　　　　　　　（　　）

    (エ) Mr. Lindblad thought the travel companies should care about the natural

        environment.　　　　　　　　　　　　　　　　　　　　　　　（　　）

Lesson 13 関係詞①

Grammar 目標 ➡ 7分

1 ( )内に、下のa.～d.から適当なものを選び、記号を補いなさい。 （各2点）

1. The police have caught the man ( ).

2. I don't like stories ( ).

3. What happened to the pictures ( )?

4. Romeo and Juliet were two lovers ( ).

　　a. that were on the wall 　　　　b. who stole my car

　　c. whose parents hated each other 　　d. which have unhappy endings

2 例にならって、第2文を完成しなさい。 （各4点）

　例：You lost the keys.　　Have you found the keys …?

　　　→Have you found the keys you lost?

1. You cooked the meal.　　The meal … was excellent.

_____

2. You told me about the hotel.　　What's the name of the hotel …?

_____

3. I slept in the bed last night.　　The bed … wasn't very comfortable.

_____

Writing 目標 ➡ 5分

3 ( )内に与えられた語句を並べかえて、英文を完成しなさい。 （各4点）

1. あなたが車を借りた男の人の名前は？

　What's the name of (borrowed / car / the man / whose / you)?

_____

2. これは私が今までに食べた中で最高のハンバーガーだ。

　This is (eaten / ever / I've / the best hamburger / that).

_____

3. 結局、私たちが待っていたバスは来なかった。

　After all, (for / the bus / waiting / we / were) didn't arrive.

_____

CAN-DO List □ 〈知識・技能〉関係代名詞（主格・所有格、目的格の省略）を適切に活用することができる。

Listening

目標 ➡ 5分   テーマ 動物 GTEC® 🔊 34〜35

4 それぞれの問いについて対話を聞き、答えとして最も適当なものを一つずつ選びなさい。(各5点)

1. 男性は今何をしていますか。

2. イヌの小さな斑点はどこにありますか。

Rapid Reading

目標 ➡ 5分   テーマ 動物 共通テスト

5 メッセージを読み取って、問いに対する答えとして最も適当なものを一つずつ選びなさい。

(各5点)

> **Jim**
>
> Hey, Sasha.　I'm in a pet grooming studio with Lush.　I forgot how long his hair should be, so could you tell me again?　Did you say his body hair should be cut to 5mm?
>
> 10:25

> **Sasha**
>
> No, that's just for his head and ears.　The hair of his body and legs should be 3mm.　I forgot to tell you about his tail hair. Please have it cut to the same length as last time.
>
> 10:29

> **Jim**
>
> Got it!　Thank you.　Then, is it OK for you to pick us up in an hour?
>
> 10:31

1. How long will Lush's body hair be?

　① It will be 3mm long.　　② It will be 5mm long.

　③ It will be the same length as last time.　④ It will remain the same length as it is now.

2. When will Sasha pick Jim and Lush up?

　① As soon as possible.　　② At around 10:30.

　③ At around 11:30.　　④ At around 13:30.

Reading　目標 → 20分　文法項目 関係代名詞　テーマ 動物　🔊 36

速 読問題 次の英文を2.5分で読んで、1. の問いに答えなさい。

　Pets are *incredibly well loved in America: according to a 2015 Harris survey, 95% of owners think of their animals as members of the family. About half buy them birthday presents. People who have pets tend to have lower blood pressure, heart rates and heart-disease risks than others. (1)Those benefits may come from the
5　exercise (A)that playing and walking require and from the stress relief of having a steady best friend.

　Scientists are now *digging up evidence (B)that animals can also help improve mental health. Though there have been few studies so far, the benefits are so impressive (C)that hospitals are allowing pet therapy to be used, together with
10　*conventional medicine. "(2)It used to be one of the impossible things to think of in a hospital," says Alan Beck, director of the Center for the Human-Animal Bond at Purdue University. "Now, I don't know of any major children's hospital that doesn't have at least some kind of animal program."

　The rise of animal therapy *is backed by serious science showing that social support
15　— a proven *antidote to anxiety and loneliness — can (3)come on four legs, not just two. (4)More research is needed before scientists know exactly why it works and how much animal interaction is needed for the best results. But studies do show (D)that animals have a place in medicine and in mental well-being. "The data is strong," Beck says. "If you look at what animals do for people and how we interact with them, it's not
20　surprising at all."

(251 words)

---

1 incredibly [ɪnkrédəb(ə)li]：驚くほど　　7 dig up ...：…を探し集める
10 conventional [kənvénʃ(ə)n(ə)l]：従来の　　14 be backed by ...：…に裏打ちされる
15 antidote [ǽntidòʊt]：解消法

CAN-DO List　☐ 〈知識・技能〉関係代名詞について理解できる。
　　　　　　　☐ 〈思考力・判断力・表現力〉ペットセラピーの特徴について的確に理解できる。

1. この英文のタイトルとして最も適当なものを、次の a.～ d.から選びなさい。　　　　（5点）

　　a. Recent Trend in Pet Ownership in the U.S.

　　b. Social Therapy for People Losing their Pets

　　c. The Relation between Animals and Medical Care

　　d. The Scientific Research on Animal Mental Health

精 読問題 もう一度英文を読んで、次の問いに答えなさい。

2. **文法** 波線部(A)～(D)の that のうち、関係代名詞の that を一つ選び、記号で答えなさい。　（4点）

　　（　　　　　）

3. 下線部(1)が指すものを具体的に日本語で説明しなさい。　　　　　　　　　　　（7点）

　　_____

4. 下線部(2)が指しているものを具体的に表した箇所を、本文中から2語で抜き出しなさい。　（7点）

　　（　　　　　）（　　　　　　　）

5. 下線部(3)は具体的にどういうことですか。four legs と two が表すものをそれぞれ明らかにして、日本語で説明しなさい。　　　　　　　　　　　　　　　　　　　　　　　　　　（8点）

　　_____

　　_____

6. 下線部(4)について、研究がもっと必要なのは何をするためですか。日本語で説明しなさい。（7点）

　　_____

7. **全体把握** 本文の内容と合っているものにはT、合っていないものにはFと答えなさい。（各2点）

　　(ア) Few of the owners were given their pet as a birthday present.　　（　　　　）

　　(イ) Animals seem useful in improving human mental health.　　（　　　　）

　　(ウ) If pet therapy is used, there is no need for conventional medicine.　　（　　　　）

　　(エ) The use of pet therapy in hospitals was not possible in the past.　　（　　　　）

　　(オ) Enough research has already been done on animal therapy.　　（　　　　）

Lesson 14 関係詞②

Grammar 目標 ➡ 7分

1 ( )内に、下のa.～e.から適当なものを選び、記号を補いなさい。 (各2点)

1. You never let me do ( ).

2. The teacher tested the students to see if they remembered ( ).

3. Are you sorry for ( )?

4. What he did and ( ) were not the same.

5. Everything ( ) at the meeting was true.

 a. what I want to do   b. what he said   c. what they had learned

 d. what you did   e. that he said

2 ☐内から適当なものを選び、＿＿を補って英文を完成しなさい。 (各3点)

where / when	+	he was born / the weather is usually hottest / we first met / we stayed

1. Do you remember the hotel _____ ?

2. Do you remember the day _____ ?

3. He still lives in the town _____ .

4. August is the month _____ .

Writing 目標 ➡ 3分

3 ( )内に与えられた語句を並べかえて、英文を完成しなさい。 (各4点)

1. その広告に書いてあることは本当ではない。

 (is / not / says / that advertisement / what) true.

_____

2. きみがしたことを見たら、彼女は怒るでしょう。

 When (done / sees / she / what / you've), she will be angry.

_____

3. 車の走っていない町に住みたいものだ。

 I'd like to live in (a town / are / no cars / there / where).

_____

CAN-DO List ☐ 🔊 〈知識・技能〉関係代名詞 what、関係副詞を適切に活用することができる。

Listening

目標 ➡ 5分　　　　　　　　テーマ 異文化理解　 37

4 長めの英文を聞き、問いの答えとして最も適当なものを一つずつ選びなさい。　　（各5点）

1. Which is true about the number of foreign people who visited Japan in 2016?

　① About 4 million Chinese people visited Japan.

　② About 6 million Korean people visited Japan.

　③ Nearly half of all visitors came from China.

　④ Nearly half of all visitors came from China and Korea.

2. Which is true according to the speaker's talk?

　① It's important for Chinese people to eat up all the food served.

　② Korean people have the same custom of leftovers as Japanese have.

　③ It's polite of Chinese people to leave some food after finishing eating.

　④ It's natural to criticize the foreign people who leave the food.

Rapid Reading

目標 ➡ 5分　　　　　　　　テーマ 情報化社会　英検®

5 （1）・（2）に入れるのに最も適当なものを一つずつ選びなさい。　　（各5点）

　People today may feel that success *depends heavily on their ability to access information quickly and easily.　They may fear that （　1　） will put them at a *disadvantage.　What we have to keep in mind, though, is that collecting and *storing information is not the same as *acquiring knowledge, understanding, or wisdom.　The *challenge facing us now is （　2　） for the *benefit of the whole of society.

> ¹depend on ...： …次第である、…によって決まる　　³disadvantage [dìsədvǽntidʒ]：不利な立場
> ³store： …を蓄える　　⁴acquire [əkwáiər]：…を獲得する
> ⁵challenge [tʃǽlɪn(d)ʒ]：課題、難問　　⁵benefit [bénɪfɪt]：利益

1. ① being able to do so　　　　　　② being unable to do so

　③ having to do so　　　　　　　　④ not having to do so

2. ① how to collect and store as much information as possible

　② how to get used to the worldwide flow of information

　③ how to put information to the best possible use

　④ how to stop the advance of information technology

速 読問題 次の英文を2.5分で読んで、1. の問いに答えなさい。

In this modern age, communication is so fast that it is almost instant. People's lives have been changed because of the immediate spread of news. Sometimes the speed is so rapid that (1)it does not allow people time to think. For example, leaders of countries have only minutes, or at most hours, to consider all the parts of a problem. They are

5 expected to answer immediately. Once they had days and weeks to think before making decisions.

The speed of communication means that people all over the world have (2)a new responsibility. People in different countries must try harder to understand each other. For example, people with different religions must try to understand each other's beliefs

10 and values even if they do not accept them. Sometimes their cultures are quite different. (3)What one group considers a normal part of life is strange to another culture. In some cases, a normal part of one culture might be bad or impolite to other people. That kind of difference creates a possibility for misunderstanding. People must learn not to judge others, but to accept them (4)as they are. Then understanding

15 between cultures can be better. Misunderstandings can be avoided.

Misunderstandings as a result of the increase in fast communication can cause serious problems. Therefore, good communication between and across cultures is important. Better (5)cross-cultural communication is necessary for peace in the world. (6)As the world grows smaller, people must learn to talk to each other better,

20 not just faster. (246 words)

CAN-DO List ☐ 〈知識・技能〉関係代名詞 what について理解できる。
☐ 〈思考力・判断力・表現力〉情報化社会で必要なことについて的確に理解できる。

	Grammar	Writing	Listening	Rapid Reading	Reading	Total
	/22	/12	/10	/10	/46	/100

1. この英文で主に述べられているものを、次のa.～d.から選びなさい。　　　　　（5点）

 a．コミュニケーションのスピード化にともなう誤解の可能性の拡大

 b．情報化社会にともなう世界の画一化の危険

 c．情報社会における異文化間の相互理解の重要性

 d．伝達のスピード化にともなう情報の正確性の重要性

精 読問題 もう一度英文を読んで、次の問いに答えなさい。

2. 下線部(1)の具体的な例としてどんなことが挙げられていますか。日本語で説明しなさい。　（7点）

_____

_____

3. 下線部(2)の具体的な内容を、日本語で簡潔にまとめなさい。　　　　　　　　（7点）

_____

4. 文法 下線部(3)がもたらすものを本文中から4語で抜き出しなさい。　　　　（6点）

 (　　　　　) (　　　　　) (　　　　　) (　　　　　)

5. 下線部(4)、(6)のas とほぼ同じ意味・用法のas を含む文を、それぞれ次のa.～d.から一つずつ選びなさい。　　　　　　　　　　　　　　　　　　　　　　　　　　　　（各2点）

 a．As I didn't have enough money for a taxi, I had to walk home.

 b．As the manager, she has to make many important decisions.

 c．As the sun goes higher, our shadows become shorter.

 d．Why didn't you do as I told you to do it?　　(4) (　　　　)　(6) (　　　　)

6. 下線部(5)とほぼ同じ内容を表している箇所を本文中から抜き出しなさい。　　（5点）

_____

7. 全体把握 本文の内容と合っているものにはT、合っていないものにはFと答えなさい。（各2点）

 (ア) People's lives have been changed because they have learned that news may not be based on facts.　　　　　　　　　　　　　　　　　　　　　　　　　　(　　　)

 (イ) Leaders of countries used to have more time to make decisions.　　(　　　)

 (ウ) People all over the world must try to communicate more rapidly.　(　　　)

 (エ) People with different religions must understand each other's beliefs and values.

 　　　　　　　　　　　　　　　　　　　　　　　　　　　　　　　　(　　　)

 (オ) Cultural differences can be the cause of misunderstandings.　　(　　　)

 (カ) People today must try harder to understand each other.　　　(　　　)

Lesson 15 仮定法

1 日本語に合うように、( )内に適当な語を補いなさい。 （各2点）

1. [明日の予定を話していて] 「明日もし僕が遅れたら、僕を待たないでね。」

   If ( ) ( ) late tomorrow, don't wait for me.

2. [宝くじ売り場の前で] 「もしも宝くじで大金を得たら、きみにその半分をあげるよ。」

   If I won a big prize in a lottery, I ( ) ( ) you half of it.

3. [実際は電話番号を知らない] 「もしもジュリアの電話番号を知っていたら、電話をかけるのですが。」

   ( ) I ( ) Julia's telephone number, I would call her.

2 次の各組の文がほぼ同じ意味になるように、( )内に適語を補いなさい。 （各3点）

1. I don't have time today, so I won't go and see Judy.

   If I ( ) time today, I would go and see Judy.

2. We don't have a car, so we can't travel much.

   If we had a car, we ( ) ( ) more.

3. She is very shy, so she doesn't enjoy parties.

   If she ( ) ( ) so shy, she would enjoy parties.

4. I don't have enough money, so I'm not going to buy a car.

   If I had enough money, I ( ) ( ) a car.

3 ( )内に適語を補って、英文を完成しなさい。 （各3点）

1. だれかがあなたに卵を投げつけたら、あなたならどうしますか。

   ( ) would you do if somebody ( ) an egg at you?

2. なんてすがすがしい朝だ。午後雨になんかなりっこないよ。

   What a lovely morning! I'd be surprised ( ) it ( ) this afternoon.

3. 銃がなければ、世界はもっとよくなるのですが。

   The world would be a better place if ( ) were ( ) guns.

4. もし動物にならなければいけないとすれば、私ならトラを選ぶ。

   If I ( ) to be an animal, I'd ( ) to be a tiger.

4 長めの会話を一つ聞き、問いの答えとして最も適当なものを一つずつ選びなさい。 （各5点）

1. What is the problem they are talking about?

① There are more students who come to school on foot.

② There are more students who come to school by bike.

③ All the bikes have stickers.

④ More and more students travel a long distance.

2. Which rule would be on the poster?

① We're not allowed to use a bike without the sticker.

② We will stop using the stickers on bikes.

③ We're not allowed to use a bike if we live far from school.

④ We will put the posters on walls in the parking lots.

Rapid Reading 目標 ➡ 5分 テーマ 自転車 GTEC®

5 英文を読んで、問いの答えとして最も適当なものを一つずつ選びなさい。 （各5点）

　The bicycle has gone through one full (A) of development already. It began as a toy for rich people. Then it was a *means of *transportation. Next it became a toy again. Now the bicycle is becoming popular as a means of transportation once more.

　There are several reasons for the new popularity of bicycles. The cost of *fuel for cars is one reason. Another is the need to keep the environment clean. The third reason is a *desire for exercise. Americans are one group of people who are starting to leave their cars at home. In fact, for about thirty years bicycles have been *outselling cars. There are more than a hundred million in the United States alone.

---

²means [míːnz]：方法、手段　　²transportation [træ̀nspərtéiʃ(ə)n]：輸送、交通
⁴fuel [fjúː(ː)əl]：燃料　　⁶desire [dizáiər]：願望　　⁷outsell [àutsél]：より多く売れる

---

1. Which of the following is most appropriate to put in (A)?

① circle ② size ③ speed ④ stop

2. Which of the following pieces of information is not mentioned in the passage as a reason for bicycles' popularity?

① Bicycles do not cause any pollution.

② Bicycles do not need gas to make them go.

③ Many people ride bicycles to keep fit.

④ With a bicycle, people do not have to find a place to park.

速 読問題 次の英文を2.5分で読んで、1. の問いに答えなさい。

Some people think they have an answer to the problems of automobile crowding and dirty air in large cities.　Their answer is the bicycle.

In a great many cities, hundreds of people ride bicycles to work every day.　In New York City, some bike riders have even formed a group called "Bike for a Better City."

5　(1)They claim that if more people rode bicycles to work, there would be fewer automobiles in the downtown section of the city and therefore less dirty air from car engines.

　(2)For several years this group has been trying to get the city government to help bicycle riders.　For example, they want the city to make special lanes for bicycles only

10　on some of the main streets, because when bicycle riders must use the same lanes as cars, accidents happen.　(3)If there were special lanes, more people would use bikes.

But no bicycle lanes have been made.　Not everyone thinks they are a good idea. Taxi drivers don't like the idea; they say it will slow traffic.　(4)Some store owners on the main streets don't like the idea either; they say that if there were less traffic, they

15　would have less business.　And most people live too far from downtown to travel by bike.

The city government has not yet decided what to do.　They want to keep everyone happy.　On weekends, Central Park, the largest piece of open ground in New York, is closed to cars, and the roads may be used by bicycles only.　But "Bike for a Better City"

20　says that (5)this is not enough and that they will keep fighting to get bicycle lanes downtown.

(274 words)

CAN-DO List　□ 〈知識・技能〉仮定法過去について理解できる。
　　　　　　　□ 〈思考力・判断力・表現力〉都市環境と自転車の意義について的確に理解できる。

1. この英文のタイトルとして最も適当なものを、次のa.～d.から選びなさい。 （5点）

　　a. Bicycles for Health

　　b. Bicycle Riders in New York

　　c. Eco-friendly bicycles

　　d. To Keep Everyone Happy

精 読問題 もう一度英文を読んで、次の問いに答えなさい。

2. 文法 下線部(1)の主張の具体的な内容を日本語で説明しなさい。 （8点）

_____

3. 下線部(2)について、このグループは市当局に具体的にはどのようなことを要請していますか。日本語で説明しなさい。 （7点）

_____

4. 下線部(3)はだれの考えですか。次のa.～d.から最も適当なものを選び、記号で答えなさい。 （3点）

　　a. taxi drivers　　　　　　　　b. "Bike for a Better City"

　　c. people who live far from downtown　　d. the city government

5. 文法 下線部(4)の理由を日本語で説明しなさい。 （7点）

_____

6. 下線部(5)の具体的な内容を、日本語で説明しなさい。 （8点）

_____

7. 全体把握 本文の内容と合っているものにはT、合っていないものにはFと答えなさい。（各2点）

　(ア) Some people think the bicycle will solve the problems of automobile crowding and dirty air in large cities. （　　）

　(イ) Bicycles are very popular in New York because New York has good and safe roads for bicycles only. （　　）

　(ウ) "Bike for a Better City" is a group organized by the city government. （　　）

　(エ) The city government also wants more people to use bicycles instead of cars. （　　）

　(オ) Some people don't think that bicycle lanes are a good idea. （　　）

　(カ) The city government wants to keep everyone happy and has not yet decided what to do. （　　）

Sources

■Listening

Lesson 4（グラフ）

財務省貿易統計(2020年)より作成

■Rapid Reading

Lesson 6

MIKULECKY, BEATRICE S.；JEFFRIES, LINDA, MORE READING POWER, 1st Ed.,
©1996. Reprinted by permission of Pearson Education, Inc., New York, New York.

■Reading

Lesson 5

Excerpts from MY SIDE OF THE MOUNTAIN by Jean Craighead George,
copyright ©1959, renewed ©1987 by Jean Craighead George.　Used by permission of Dutton Children's
Books,
an imprint of Penguin Young Readers Group, a division of Penguin Random House LLC.　All rights
reserved.

Lesson 7

渋谷教育学園幕張中学校・高等学校　2021年度入学試験問題(一部改変)

Lesson 10

"The Dior Kiss" by Joe Anne Ong, originally published in Reader's Digest Asia.
Copyright ©2009 by Trusted Media Brands, Inc.　Used by permission.　All rights reserved.

Lesson 11

天理大学　2021年度入学試験問題(一部改変)

Lesson 13

From TIME.　©2018 TIME USA LLC..　All rights reserved.　Used under license.